DR. POSIN'S GIANTS

Men of Science

If I have seen further than others, it is only because I have stood on the shoulders of giants who have come before me.

ISAAC NEWTON

DR. POSIN'S GIANTS

Men of Science

by

DAN Q. POSIN

with illustrations by the author

R O W, P E T E R S O N A N D C O M P A N Y
Evanston, Illinois   Elmsford, New York

*The drawings in this book are by the author, Dr. Dan Q. Posin,
who, in the classroom and on television, clarifies scientific concepts
with his sketches and diagrams.*

ACKNOWLEDGMENTS

I wish to thank Chicago's educational television station WTTW—
Window To The World—where the programs upon which this book is
based were produced. I also have in mind Bud Ellingwood, producer, and
Tom Hull and Jim McPharlin, my directors. It is a pleasure to acknowl-
edge the support of the National Educational Television and Radio Center
in helping to shape the programs, in having them taped, and in making
them available nationally. I wish to thank also Jim Taylor, Director of
Radio and Television for De Paul University, for much encouragement
through the years.

My thanks go also to TV viewers who have written and phoned their
reactions as the programs progressed.

DAN Q. POSIN

Contents

Archimedes

Archimedes

c. 2 8 7 - 2 1 2 B.C.

The Roman soldier stood with his club raised over the old man who sat drawing mathematical figures in the tray of dust.

"Get up!" ordered the soldier. "Move."

The old man continued to draw.

"I must finish this proof," he said, bending lower over the fine drawing dust.

The Roman soldier, who with his hordes had invaded the island of Sicily and conquered the city of Syracuse, stood glowering. For a moment he hesitated.

The old man, the Greek mathematician, Archimedes, continued to sketch. . . .

Archimedes had done much in his lifetime.

There was the day when he jumped out of the bathtub and started running down the street, shouting, "Eureka! Eureka! I have found it! I have found it!"

What had he found?

Archimedes had found a way to solve a puzzle. Suddenly, as he sank into his tub, the solution came to him. Archimedes noted how the water in the tub rose as he settled himself. He then saw plainly how to get an answer to an important question—a question put to him by King Hieron. Sooner or later, Archimedes knew, he must answer the King's question.

Doubt and suspicion tormented the King. He suspected that his goldsmith was gypping him. The King had ordered a solid gold crown from the goldsmith. On receiving the crown, King Hieron began to worry. The goldsmith, he suspected, had mixed silver with the gold.

"Find out," requested the King of Archimedes.
"Is there silver in my crown?"

To answer this question, Archimedes first put the crown into a bowl full of water. The crown sank to the bottom. As it sank, the crown caused some water to overflow from the bowl. The water spilled from the bowl into another container. Archimedes carefully measured the amount of the overflow.

Next Archimedes measured out a portion of gold equal to the weight of the crown. He then put the gold into the

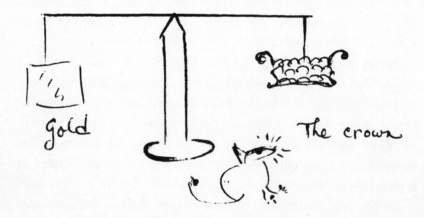

gold   The crown

same bowl filled with water. Again some water overflowed. But the overflow from the gold was smaller than from the crown. Thus, Archimedes could see the crown contained an

4

impurity. Otherwise, the crown and the gold would have displaced the same amount of water.

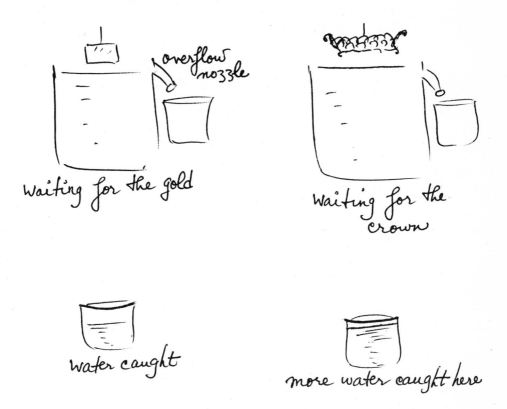

waiting for the gold

waiting for the crown

water caught

more water caught here

Archimedes also weighed out some silver. He noted how much water a certain amount of silver displaces. By checking and rechecking, he determined how much gold and how much silver the crown contained.

What happened to the goldsmith? The record does not show. But he probably lost *his* crown. Or maybe he became a silversmith.

In his experiment, Archimedes dealt with a phenomenon we now call *specific gravity*. Specific gravity is a comparison of the density of a substance with the density of water. Density, in turn, denotes the weight of a standard volume of a substance.

A pint of gold, for example, weighs about 19 pounds. A pint of water weighs about one pound. Thus, the specific gravity of gold is about 19. The specific gravity of silver is about 10. As Archimedes knew, gold is heavier (or more dense) than silver.

Archimedes, as the story goes, had the king's crown in mind when he stepped from his tub. But his bath on this particular day might very well have been the source of further insight. He made another important discovery known as *Archimedes' Principle.*

A body under water, Archimedes noted, is lighter than ordinarily. A force known as *buoyancy* holds the body up.

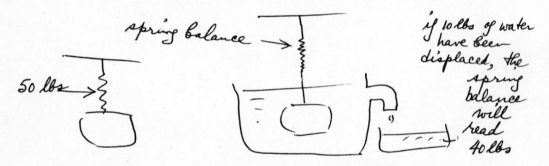

Archimedes explained this buoyancy. His principle states that, *When a body is placed in a fluid, the weight it seems to lose is equal to the weight of the fluid it displaces.* His principle explains why bodies can float. A body floats when the weight of the fluid it displaces equals its own weight.

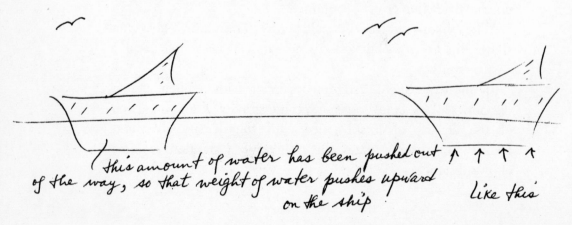

As a mathematician, Archimedes ranks among the greatest. He was the first one really to understand the *circle*. What is there to understand? For one thing, how long is the circle all the way around if its diameter is five inches? What, then, is the circumference? How much?

Until Archimedes thought the problem through, no one could answer these questions. Everyone, you might say, went around in circles, and got no where. Now we know.

Of course, today, the children in school say, "Diameter multiplied by $\frac{22}{7}$."

Or, "D × $3\frac{1}{7}$."

Or, they might say, "D × pi."

Yes, but who figured out this $\frac{22}{7}$? Who discovered this value we call *pi*?

Archimedes.

How did he do it? How did he find out the ratio of the circumference to the diameter? How did he settle upon the figure $\frac{22}{7}$, or $3\frac{1}{7}$, or 3.1428.

First, let us start with a six-sided figure drawn in a circle:

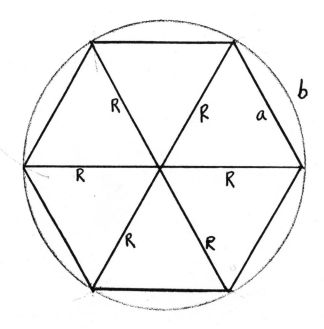

R is the radius. If we know R, it is easy to get a. Everyone in Archimedes' time knew how to work with triangles. It is the circle's length that they could not calculate. Now, can we say that b is equal to a? Not quite.

The arc b must be longer than the chord a. The idea, however, is this: Archimedes planned to consider a figure of *many* sides inside the circle. Then the chord a and the arc b would be almost the same length. Since it is easy to add up mathematically all the lengths of chords, he would just about have the length of the circle itself, in this manner:

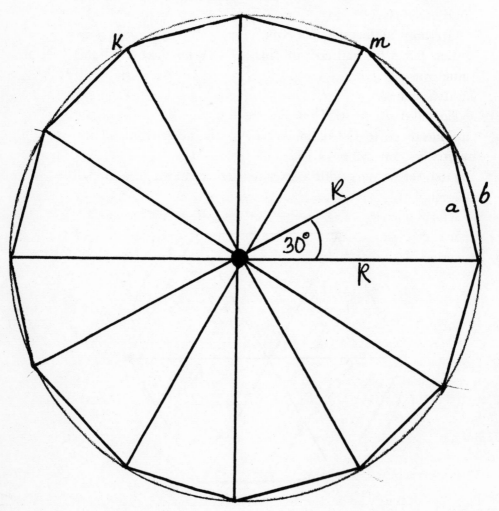

Draw a figure of twelve sides. Now any *a* is almost equal to *b*. And Archimedes—as well as other mathematicians—knew how to get the length *a* by working with the triangle *RRa*. So it went.

By considering polygons with more and more sides, Archimedes could get an *a* extremely close to the value of a *b*. Then he drew an *external* polygon, touching the circle. The *a*'s now fell outside the circle, and were slightly more than the *b*'s in value. Archimedes now had two important values— the value of *a*'s that almost equalled the *b*'s and the value of *a*'s that was a little more than the *b*'s.

Archimedes knew the circumference, then, would lie between these two values. From the circumference, he computed the ratio to the diameter at nearly $3\frac{1}{7}$. Or, to be exact, he determined the ratio of the circumference to the diameter to be less than $3\frac{1}{7}$ and greater than $3\frac{10}{71}$.

Forever curious, Archimedes advanced the study of geometry further with a breakdown of the cone. By dissecting the cone, he singled out various types of curves—the ellipse, the parabola, and the hyperbola.

These curves are especially important today. They have a space-age significance, all of which reminds us that the discoveries of great minds are timeless. Without his knowledge

Do you know how to draw an ellipse?

Get 2 thumb tacks, a piece of string and a pencil

of the ellipse, the parabola, and the hyperbola, the space technologist could never put a satellite in a predetermined orbit. He could never track it once it was in orbit.

Here are the curves:

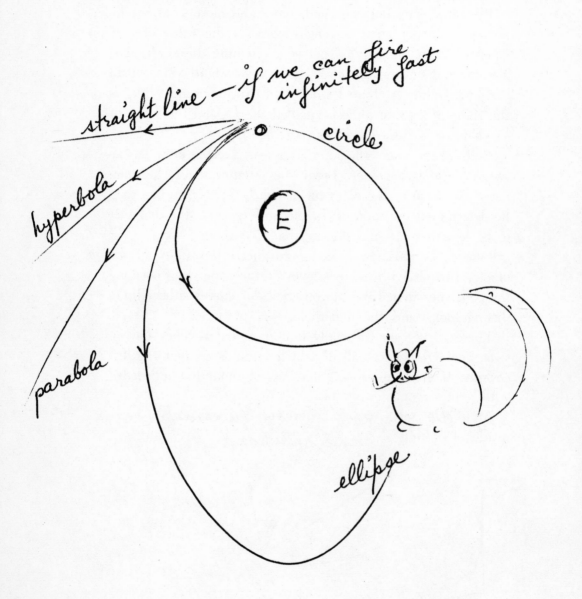

straight line — if we can fire infinitely fast

circle

hyperbola

E

parabola

ellipse

And the cone:

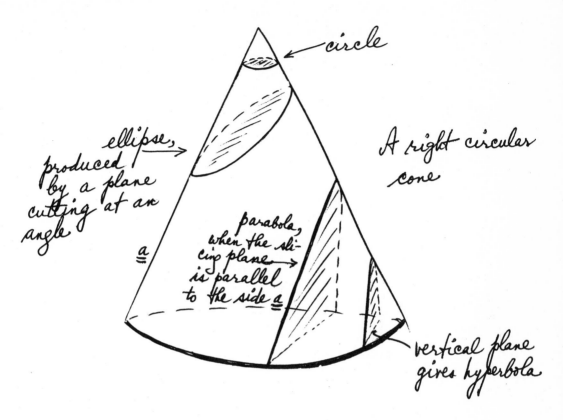

circle

A right circular cone

ellipse, produced by a plane cutting at an angle

a

parabola, when the slicing plane is parallel to the side a

vertical plane gives hyperbola

Now, how could you get a couple of *straight lines*? How, with a plane, would you have to slice the cone?

Archimedes also worked with cylinders, and with spheres inside of cylinders.

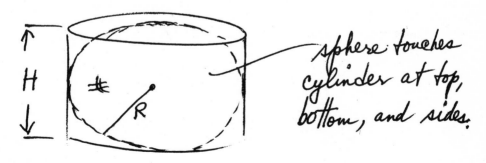

H

R

sphere touches cylinder at top, bottom, and sides.

He solved this problem: *How much is the space taken up by the cylinder, compared with the space taken up by the sphere?* He got this result

Volume of cylinder, $\pi R^2 H$, or $2\pi R^3$, since $H = 2R$
Volume of sphere, $\frac{4}{3}\pi R^3$

Therefore: the ratio is

$$\frac{2\pi R^3}{\frac{4}{3}\pi R^3}, \text{ or } \frac{3}{2}$$

Archimedes, by his particularly acute reckoning, which is a forerunner of the calculus, calculated the areas of curved surfaces.

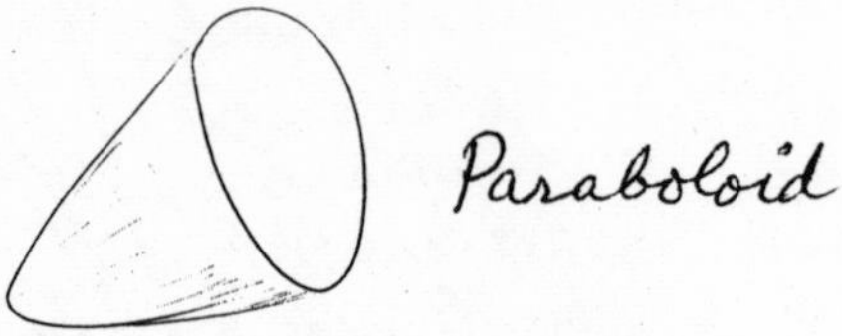

Paraboloid

Then, there was Archimedes' work with the lever. He understood clearly the law of the lever—a law that enables men to lift loads that otherwise might be immovable.

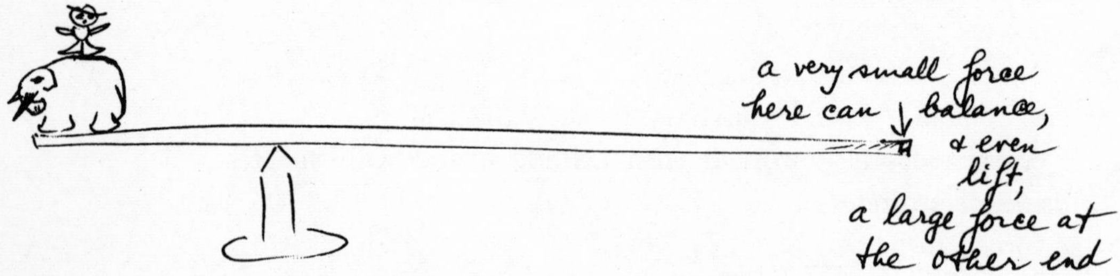

a very small force here can balance, & even lift, a large force at the other end

Archimedes saw that a small force at one end of a lever can balance and even lift a large force at the other end. By using a lever, we can "gain" in force. However, if we want to lift the heavy object, we will "lose" in distance. The right end must be pushed far down simply to lift the left end up a little.

12

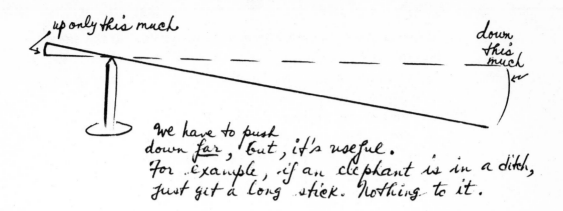

up only this much

down this much

we have to push down far, but, it's useful. For example, if an elephant is in a ditch, just get a long stick. Nothing to it.

So proud was Archimedes of the *Principle of the Lever* that he proclaimed, "Give me a place to stand and I will move the earth."

Let's give him a place to stand:

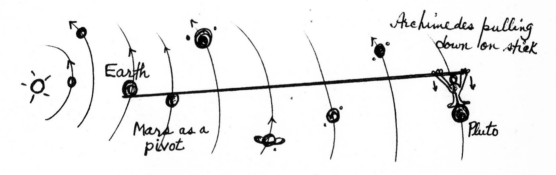

Archimedes pulling down on stick

Earth

Mars as a pivot

Pluto

Do you see anything impractical about this earth lifting?

Archimedes, occasionally, was a practical man. In fact, he was forced to be practical. The Romans were attacking Syracuse, the Greek city-state on the island of Sicily, where Archimedes lived with his fellow Greek citizens.

Using the *Principle of the Lever,* Archimedes designed a gigantic catapult for Syracusan forces. With this catapult, the defenders of Syracuse repelled the attacking Romans. The stones hurled from the catapult rained down on the approaching Roman ships, forcing the invaders to retreat in panic.

13

A few ships reached the shores of Sicily. But, so the story goes, the Syracusans upended and sank these ships with large cranes designed by Archimedes. An intricate pulley system worked the cranes.

Archimedes is supposed to have defended his island with large curved mirrors. According to the legend, he used the mirrors to focus the sun's rays on approaching enemy ships. Trapped in the searing heat, the ships caught fire and burned.

In all probability, there is no truth to this story. There were no large curved mirrors in those times. Still, one could have arranged small plane mirrors onto a paraboloidal surface.

But is it likely that an enemy would have sailed into the focal point? Would a crafty invader have lingered stupidly in the sunlight only to be fried?

With Archimedes' help, the Syracusans staved off the Romans for several years. But, in time, the massive forces from across the waters overwhelmed the brave defenders. The Romans swarmed onto the island, marching triumphantly into Syracuse.

"Did you hear me?" bellowed the soldier. "Rise."

"Let me finish," Archimedes repeated. "Stand away!"

The soldier lifted his club higher.

"Come on!" he snapped. "Come on, old man, move! Or else . . . "

Archimedes turned back to his work.

"I'm going to finish this," he said.

The soldier brought the club crashing down on the old man's head.

On the floor lay the body of Archimedes, greatest mathematician of antiquity.

When the people of Syracuse buried Archimedes, they erected over his grave a sphere inscribed within a cylinder, symbols of the pure mathematical beauty that Archimedes had created.

From the floor of a room in Pompeii

Hipparchus

Hipparchus

fl. 146-127 B.C.

In distant space, radio signals are traveling between stars.
Maybe some of these signals are intelligible messages. We
know that the stars are suns. Some of them may have good,
habitable earths around them—earths with intelligent beings
who are communicating with each other across space.

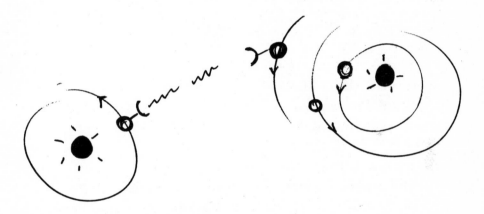

Our huge optical telescopes have brought us close to far
away galaxies. And radio telescopes have taken us even deeper
into space. Their big, parabolic dishes have picked up radio
waves from gaseous clouds and from exploding stars, and from
galaxies billions of light years away.

But imagine a man working on Planet Earth with no telescope at all, yet learning a great deal about the stars.

There *was* such a man. His name was Hipparchus. Born
in Nicaea near the sea of Marmara, this Greek astronomer
used nothing more than a sighting tube, without lenses at all,
for they were unknown in his time.

17

Working with unrelenting devotion, Hipparchus became one of the greatest mathematicians and astronomers. He studied the stars so carefully that he was able to list correctly according to their brightness about one thousand suns of space. These observations he carried out in Bithynia, in Rhodes, and in Alexandria.

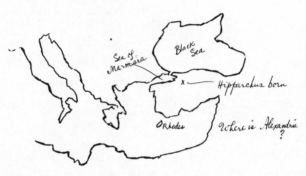

We learn about Hipparchus from the writers of the times, particularly from Strabo, and also from the later astronomer, Ptolemy. Ptolemy (*fl.* A.D. 127-151) writes with admiration of Hipparchus in his work, *The Almagest*. The generous Ptolemy says of Hipparchus, "He was a man loving work and loving the truth."

Ptolemy well knew how great a work Hipparchus had performed. For, in setting forth his own astronomical system, Ptolemy referred to the observations and findings of Hipparchus.

2

What would you need if you were asked to locate the brightest stars?

Could you tell others how to find these stars once you had located them? Would it not be helpful to be able to say, "Go this far to the right, that far to the left, and this far up. And there it is?"

Do we not give directions in some such way? Hipparchus in like manner worked out a system for the heavens and its starry inhabitants. He invented a special device for mapping the skies and locating the stars. Hipparchus called his instrument a "celestial sphere."

Hipparchus imagined earth to be surrounded by a vast heavenly sphere dotted with stars. He drew curves conforming to latitudes and longitudes on this celestial sphere. Thus, he could locate the stars in relation to latitudes and longitudes. He could indicate each location with a number.

The celestial sphere was a simple device. But it took the initiative and the imagination of such a one as Hipparchus to design it. Only a man with an affection and an appreciation for the beauties of the universe could have felt the need for such an instrument. With the aid of his sphere, Hipparchus accurately reproduced the heavens in miniature.

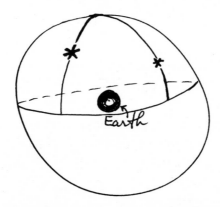

Perhaps you may want to look up descriptions of other instruments Hipparchus used—devices such as the *Diopter,* the *parallactic instrument,* and the *mural quadrant.* There is reason to believe that he also used the *meridian circle* and the *astrolabon organon.*

It was Hipparchus who first divided an instrumental circle into 360°. Why do you suppose Hipparchus used 360 divisions, or degrees? Why not 300? Or 100? Or 320?

In all fairness, we must give credit to the astronomer
Hypsicles of Alexandria, who came before Hipparchus,
and who divided the circle of the earth's orbit around the
sun into 360°. (Hypsicles did not know that the earth
travels around the sun. It was the sun, he thought, which
travels around the earth. Accordingly, he divided his "ecliptic" into 360°.)

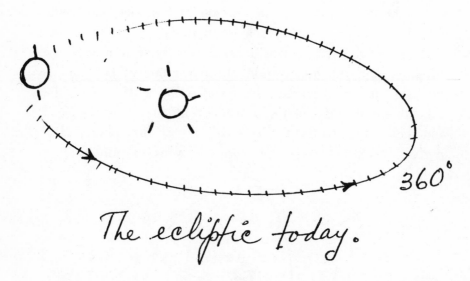

The ecliptic today.

The indefatigable Hipparchus struggled for years to make
sense of the work of previous astronomers. He examined
closely the theories of Eudoxus, who had done much in the
first half of the fourth century B.C., and also studied in great
detail the work of Apollonius, who had labored at the end of
the third century B.C.

Eudoxus and Apollonius had tried to explain the apparent
irregular motions of the moon, sun, and planets, but they got
nowhere, because they had assumed that the earth was standing still as the center of the universe, while everything else
moved around the central earth.

How can you make sense of the motions of the heavenly
bodies if you take the wrong spot as the point of reference?

Both Eudoxus and Apollonius were especially baffled by the strange back-going of the planets. Here is an example (pretend you think the earth is standing still):

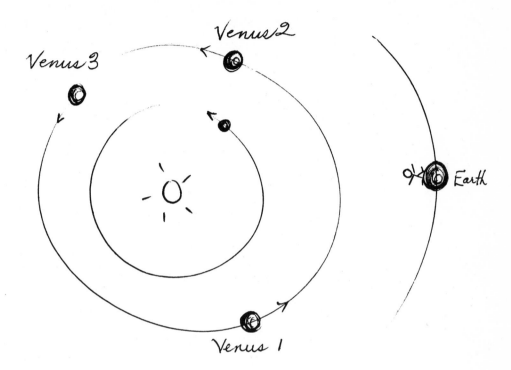

At 1, Venus seems to the left of the observer on earth. At 2, Venus seems to be to the right. At 3, the planet is going to the left again. What is going on? Remember, you do not know Venus is going around the sun. Furthermore, the earth really has been moving, but you ignored its movement! So what will the motion of Venus seem like?

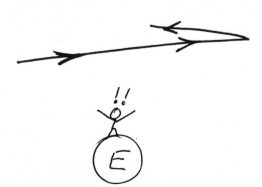

We have to admit that someone even in these times had come forth with the idea that the sun stood still and the planets orbited around it, but the overworked Hipparchus would not go for this theory. He rejected the heliocentric theory of Aristarchus of Samos, and hung on to the geocentric ideas, striving to save the entire misdirected conception along with the vast amount of off-kilter observations.

Hipparchus passed on the foundations of this confused approach to Ptolemy, who made the confusion rigorous, complete, and unassailable. As a result, this distorted conception of the universe—this celestial madness—persisted for fifteen hundred years.

(Did you know that there is today a group of people who persist in believing that the earth is flat? And, of course, they have formed an organization called "The Flat-Earthers.")

Aristarchus suggested that the planets go around the sun in *circles*. His suggestion is not right, since the orbits are ellipses, and unless we insist on ellipses, we do not really solve the celestial puzzle. It was, however, a good try.

3

The greatest discovery that Hipparchus made was this: *The tip of the axis of the earth, through the centuries, makes a circle in the heavens.*

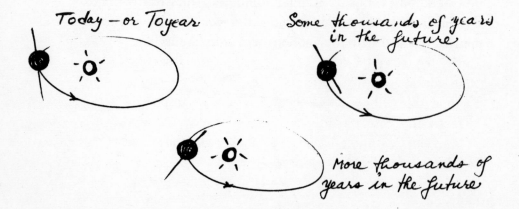

Today — or Toyear

Some thousands of years in the future

More thousands of years in the future

Can you visualize the curve traced by the end of the extended axis in the heavens? It is a circle, traced out complete in 26,000 years.

This motion is just like that of a top which is spinning on the earth's surface. The top is tipping and tracing a curve with the end of its axis. This movement is called *precession*. The top is pulled downward by gravity, but so long as it spins, it does not fall. Instead, it goes around— precesses.

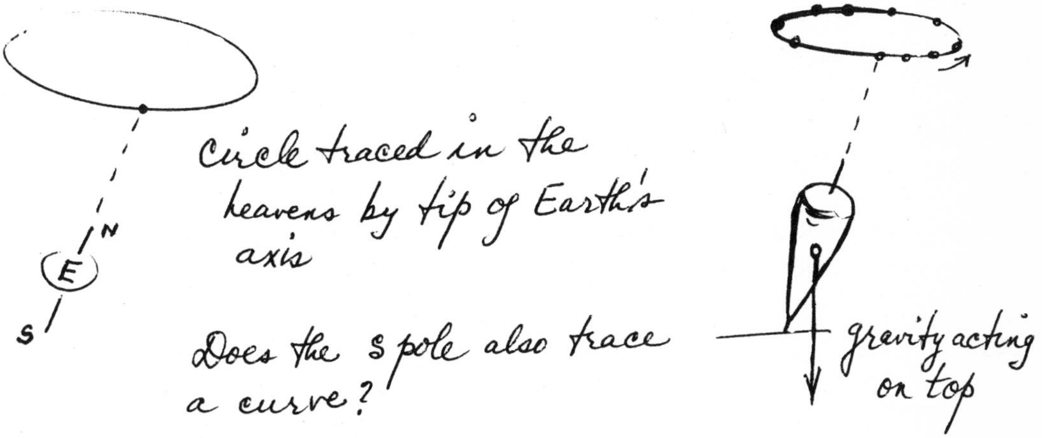

Circle traced in the heavens by tip of Earth's axis

N

E

S

Does the s pole also trace a curve?

gravity acting on top

The top makes a complete precessional revolution rather quickly. The earth takes 26,000 years. In A.D. 13,000, earth's axis will point almost at the star Vega, which thereupon will be our polestar. But, 26,000 years from now, we shall have Polaris back.

In the case of the spinning top, the precession is caused by the pull of earth's gravity. For the earth, the precession results from the pull of the moon and the sun upon the earth's equatorial bulge. The moon, being closer, is responsible for about two thirds of the effect. The sun accounts for one third. This is the same division of responsibility we have in the case of tides.

You can see that, because of the precession, the portion of the sky visible from any given spot on earth slowly changes. In fact, some of the constellations stop rising above the horizon, and others come newly into view. Of course, you will have to live for thousands of years to see these changes!

This movement of the earth's axis is accompanied by the *precession of the equinoxes*. The equinox, as perhaps you recall, is the time of the year when the sun is directly over the equator. Each year the sun crosses the equator at a point west of its crossing the previous year. Or, to put it in scientific terms, there is a *precession of the equinoxes*.

Naturally, Hipparchus could not have discovered precession simply by looking at the heavens, as movement takes millenniums. One man in his own time could not hope to detect the motion by his separate sky study. Hipparchus searched the records of ancient Babylonian astronomers, who had told where the stars were in the sky. By the time of Hipparchus, these same stars were in seemingly different places because the earth had tilted in space.

4

Hipparchus loved mathematics. He was good at it, and he used it in his astronomical studies, especially in trigonometry—the relations of triangles to each other and the relations of their angles.

It is often necessary to calculate lengths of arcs in astronomy, and Hipparchus did this by using triangles, in a manner similar to the methods of Archimedes.

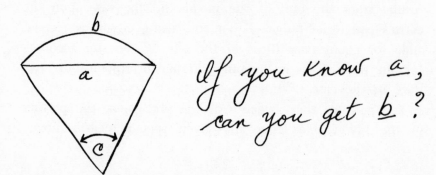

If you know $\underline{a}$, can you get $\underline{b}$?

Hipparchus made many tables for values of b, for various values of a, and for different angles c. He really put astronomy on an operating basis.

Of course, when we speak of astronomy, let's not forget the earth. Isn't the earth an astronomical body?

Hipparchus used his mathematics to do precise geographical work. He was especially interested in assigning correct longitude and latitude to places on earth. Unfortunately, he refused to accept some good calculations about the size of the earth. Eratosthenes had made these calculations about one hundred years before the time of Hipparchus, but Hipparchus did not approve of his work. There was much other previous data that he failed to accept, some of it reliable.

For the determination of longitudes on earth, Hipparchus suggested that eclipses be observed from different vantage points on earth. Then, the differences in time when the eclipse occurs would give the difference in longitude. We can see how this must be so, when we recall that the earth turns 15° per hour. Thus, one point on earth may be lined up *now* for an eclipse of the sun by the moon, then, if in one hour later another point is squarely lined up for the eclipse, the earth would have turned 15°. With this evidence, the two points on earth would be known to differ by 15° in longitude.

Hipparchus' suggestion for determining locations longitudinally was sound enough. Obviously, an eclipse would provide the necessary points of observation. But there was no scientific or political organization to effect the necessary co-operation for such a project. Hipparchus was ahead of his time.

This remarkable man did his wonderful life's work, and died. He stood on the shoulders of great investigators before him—Archimedes, Eudoxus, Apollonius. Others would stand on his shoulders, so that humanity could see further still.

Leonardo

Leonardo da Vinci

1452-1519

Is it possible to conquer gravity?

Does anti-matter exist? And, if it does exist, does it respond to anti-gravity? Could we build a spaceship out of anti-matter in order to fly from earth to another planet?

Soon we may get some surprising answers to our questions.

Many have thought throughout the ages about conquering gravity.

Perhaps you recall Daedalus and Icarus, who, in legend, attached wings to themselves, and flew away, over the Mediterranean. Icarus flew too high, too close to the sun. The hot rays melted the wax that held his wings to his body, and Icarus plunged into the sea and drowned.

Will it always be so? Will men forever be frustrated in their loftiest ambitions? Will their wings always melt? Must they inevitably plunge down from the heights to which they soar?

No, I do not think so.

One thing is sure: if we do not try, we will never make it. We must endeavor. We must reach out. Was it Browning who wrote, "Ah, but a man's reach should exceed his grasp, or what's a heaven for?"

Leonardo, from the small town of Vinci in Italy, always reached out. All his life, this boldly imaginative man reached out for the heavens themselves in science, in art, in architecture, in music, in botany, geology, anatomy, astronomy, invention.

When he designed a flying machine, Leonardo reached out literally for the heavens. His machine, suggested to him by the flight of a bird, consisted of a winglike harness. A person could put the "harness" on, and by working his wing-arms, he could fly. Or could he?

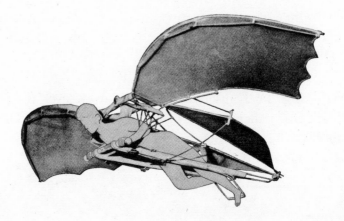

Leonardo also designed, on paper, a helicopter, and had engines been available at the time, the helicopter would have flown. Leonardo sought to conquer gravity, and today, heli-

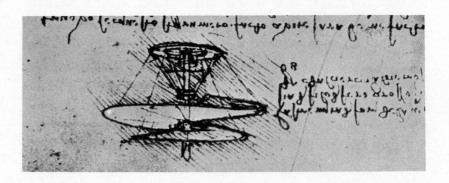

copters whirl over the United States, over the Soviet Union, and over a tiny village in Italy.

Leonardo reached in the other direction, too—below the sea. He studied fish, observed how they propelled themselves, and made sketches for submarine travel. He learned the secret of staying a long time under water.

The notes and sketches of Leonardo filled many pages, and were of an astounding character. Yet, after Leonardo died, his writing and his drawings were ignored. For years upon years, scholars passed them up, despite the fact that he presented many mathematical and engineering proofs to back up his inventions. The plain, sad fact is that his followers simply could not cope with his notebooks.

They looked upon his designs and inventions as mere fancies or whims. They referred to them as "ghiribizzi"— things that were "way out"—and spoke of them with deprecation and apology.

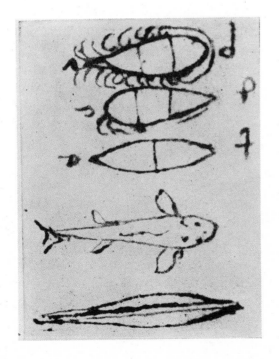

In designing a sub, why would anyone study the motion of fish?

Yes, his conceptions, designs, inventions, and experiments were "way out." So were those of Archimedes, Hipparchus, James Watt, the Wright brothers, Edison, Franklin, Einstein. . . .

Such conceptions—when the human mind and spirit are reaching for the heavens—are always way out. That's where heaven is—way out.

Only a few years ago did Leonardo's sketches and thoughts on paper come to light. But they now are available for historians and scientists to study. It is a rare experience to go to a big library and find the exciting pages called *The Notebooks of Leonardo.*

Leonardo was also way out in painting. Is anything more way out than "The Last Supper"? In boldness of conception, in artistry of execution, in excitement of original color, in depth of perception, this Leonardo creation is so far out that man, looking upon it, senses immortality.

And, of course, it was Leonardo who painted "The Mona Lisa," a woman so far out that countless art critics through the centuries have been trying to decide what it is so wondrous they see in her smile. To paint in this way, you have got to be way out. After all, this woman was only the wife of the merchant Giocondo, but Leonardo, painting her for four years to a background of music—was it the music of the spheres?—made her something infinitely subtle, ineffable, but sure and knowing, and generous and mocking.

Leonardo was always lured by the subtle, the fleeting, the unknown—this was the artist in him. Yet he searched for exact reasons and causes and logic—this was the scientist.

What a figure he cut, personally, this blessed artist and scientist and Universal Man. Of athletic stature and noble bearing, he had rich gold hair and strong masculine features. He swashed about in a rose-colored cloak.

To say that he was versatile is to say only a little, for Leonardo. He was able, adept, competent, and sure in everything. Above all, he carried a dream—that men can be great and noble and can achieve, like the very Gods.

Leonardo must have come down from Olympus. Long, long ago, I believe, he was Zeus, and he came to be reborn in the hamlet of Vinci, to walk among men, and paint them pictures, and invent them inventions. And to remind them that they, too, can soar to Olympian heights.

What does it take to belong on Mount Olympus? I wonder. Is it devotion, perfection, and force of mind?

Can we all be Leonardos?

We cannot all excel in painting, science, and architecture. But perhaps to excel is not the essence of Leonardo. Could it be that Leonardo is a quality of the mind and heart?

Was Marie Curie a Leonardo? She discovered radium, then refused to enrich herself by patenting the process of extracting the radium, and said, "It belongs to the people." And she drove an ambulance during the war.

Was Einstein a Leonardo? And Albert Schweitzer?

Talent is certainly part of it. But perhaps the *development* of whatever talent there is counts for more. Would a special attitude toward life be more important still?

"I can be. I am. I shall always be—and I shall achieve—for all humanity. For all time."

Would this have anything to do with being a Leonardo in this world?

I do not know.

I wonder.

Leonardo lived in the days when Columbus was discovering a New World. It is a curious thought: Some men discover worlds by actually traveling. Others discover them by not stirring a foot. Each man finds his own New World. Each man scales his own Everest.

Some make it higher still, to the peak of Olympus. The important thing seems to be that the New World must be "new" and shining and beckoning, not old and shabby and spiritless. Or, the important thing, perhaps, is not so much which mountains we scale. The important thing is the *direction* of the climb. The direction is *up*.

Leonardo was a sculptor. Painstaking, careful, exact, he studied the body's structure, the muscular interplay, the bearing of the head, the alignment of feet, thighs, shoulders—everything—before he began to create three-dimensional figures from materials.

He studied the laws of light and shade, probed the laws of perspective and at the same time, took in a study of optics and the physiology of the eye. Not only did he study human anatomy, but also the anatomy of animals.

Leonardo was an architect. He designed churches, town squares, and towering edifices. In Rome, he worked on the plans for St. Peter's Church and other buildings in the Vatican.

As a geologist, he gathered rocks and studied the soil, examined carefully formations within the earth, looked closely at the curve of the beach and at the waves in the sands.

Leonardo was a botanist. He gathered flowers, sketched them, probed their inner depths, sought to divine their basic principles of growth and formation. The rare plants particularly drew his attention. He observed the strange shapes of the hills and the nature of the rocks where these plants grew.

As a military engineer, Leonardo designed roads and bridges. He was at the same time a civil engineer. He devised projects for the diversion of rivers, and developed a canal system with locks. During the pestilence that swept Milan in 1484, Leonardo drew plans for rebuilding the city to give it much needed sanitary facilities.

Statics—the forces in equilibrium—fascinated Leonardo. Dynamics—the forces in action—drew his attention. Leonardo loved geometry, both for its application to problems and for itself.

How did this
operate?

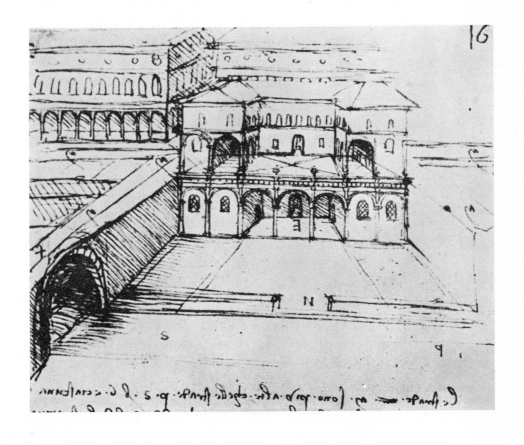

16

Look in an encyclopedia. You will find an entry for Leonardo da Vinci, all right, but you will also see the notation, "See also Aviation, Helicopter, Jet Propulsion, Painting, Parachute."

But his greatest talent, from boyhood onward, was in drawing and painting. The world is fortunate in that Leonardo had a discerning father, who took his son to Florence to study painting, sculpture, and engineering.

Leonardo has certainly been called "one of the greatest artists of the Italian Renaissance." Some people might venture to remark that Leonardo *was* the Renaissance—in large part. He has also been called "The greatest experimental scientist of his age." We won't quarrel with that.

But, despite all this, Leonardo anticipated a certain poem of our times which speaks of men walking with kings, but not losing the common touch. In his will, for example, Leonardo da Vinci asked that sixty poor men serve as torch bearers at his funeral.

It is said that no other man was as gifted in both art and science as Leonardo. Perhaps a more important clue to Leonardo than his being "gifted" in this or that is that he worked completely for the *future*. Whatever he did had to be good, and lasting.

Was Leonardo, in this way, building his immortality? Perhaps. But, the fact is, his creations and dreams had the excellence generated of love, and the permanence evolved from a seeing into the future.

Leonardo preferred to work alone. Einstein, too, worked mostly alone. He used to say, "I am a horse for single tether." Leonardo was such.

In building, devising, and creating for the future, Leonardo *seemed to sense* what future giants would discover—Galileo and the laws of motion, Newton and the mathematical harmony of the solar system, Harvey and the life-giving fluid pulsating through the veins and arteries,

Watt and the steam engine, the Wrights and flight. Leonardo had engaged in all such endeavors.

A man of great strength, yet of great gentleness, Leonardo was tender to animals as well as to human beings, and compassionate with the dispossessed of both species.

Within his grasp was material abundance, but his needs were few.

"Poor is the man of many wants," Leonardo occasionally said, and when he saw life whole, he once wrote, "As a day well spent gives joyful sleep, so does a life well spent give joyful death."

His work lives on. Other men look at it, study it, and build upon it.

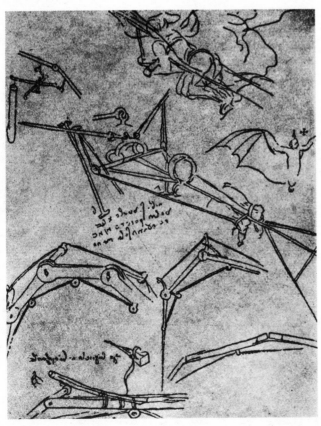

Another page from Leonardo's sketchbook. Can you explain everything?

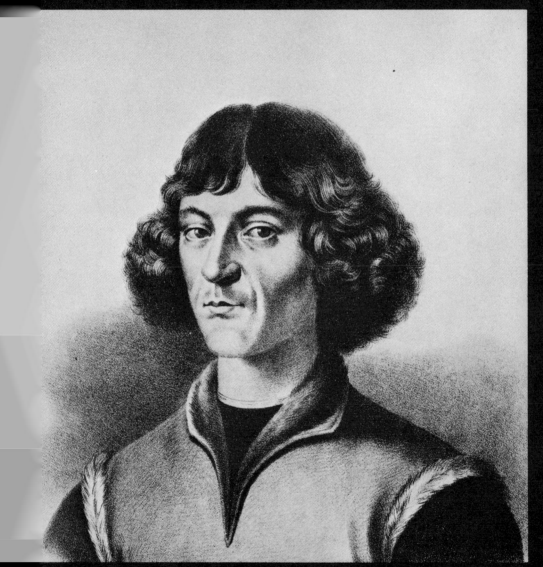

Copernicus

Nicolaus Copernicus

1473-1543

"Please tell me how to go to Mars," a schoolboy wrote.
"Is it true that I should not leave during the daytime?"

Does this seem to you like a strange question? Yet, the answer is definitely, "Yes."

Let's see exactly what the situation is.

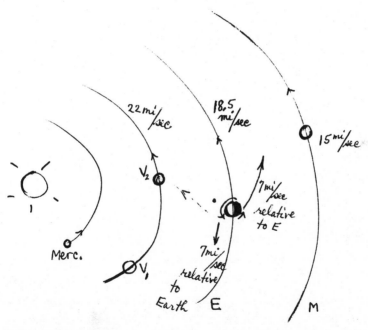

If you leave for Mars at night, as shown, you'll have the advantage of going along with the earth's rotation and also with the earth's orbital motion around the sun. At first, your velocity will be extreme. To tear away from earth, you'll need a velocity of 7 miles per second, or 25,000 mph (miles per hour). In addition, your spaceship has the free gift of 18.5 miles per second, because it was on earth, and earth has a speed of 18.5 miles per second relative to the sun. Thus, your spaceship blasts off with a total speed of 25.5 miles per second.

Earth pulls back on the spaceship as it flies along, and the sun pulls back on it, causing it to lose speed. If the ship is properly aimed, it will slow down in the vicinity of Mars to a speed of only 15 miles per second. This is exactly the proper speed for a landing on Mars. (We are taking into account the speeding-up effect which Mars will have on the ship as it approaches the planet.) As it nears the planet, there will be no relative velocity between Mars and the spaceship, and you can make a feather-light landing.

Going to Venus presents a different problem. When you go to Venus, you should leave during the day. Why? You should leave in the daytime because you must take off in the direction opposite to Earth's orbital motion. At the same time, you want to take advantage of Earth's rotational speed (about 1,100 mph at the equator). You will aim opposite the direction of Earth's revolution around the sun, but your flight will be in the direction of Earth's orbital motion at only 11.5 miles per second—Earth's speed around the sun (18.5 miles per second) minus the speed of the ship (7 miles per second), relative to Earth.

Earth will slow your spaceship somewhat by gravity's pull-back, but the sun will speed you up as you "fall" toward it. Finally, Venus will accelerate the ship a little as you get near the planet. Ultimately, the spaceship will have a speed of 22 miles per second relative to the sun. It will be moving along with Venus. With no relative velocity between the ship and Venus, you can "come in" for a soft touchdown.

How could you possibly do all this if the earth stood still? How could you take off for Mars or Venus in this manner if the sun and all the planets ran around the earth. In short, where would space travel be if you didn't know the score about the solar system?

Nicolaus Copernicus got us started.

The ancient astronomer, Ptolemy, had taught that the earth has no motions. He said the whole universe runs around the earth. That's what is meant, of course, by the term "geocentric system," "geo" standing for "earth." The earth was supposed to have been the center of it all.

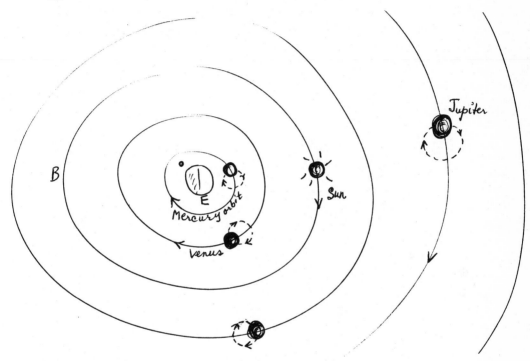

In the diagram of Ptolemy's system, the dotted circles are the extra orbits the planets seemed to make as they and the sun ran around the earth.

In the diagram, we see where the sun is to give daylight on the right-hand side of the earth. Twelve hours later the sun would have to be at B to give daylight on the left-hand side of the earth. Would it not have been simpler to have had the earth turn to get daylight on one side and nighttime on the other? As for nighttime, Ptolemy taught that the stars were embedded as gems in some sort of a huge sphere, and this sphere, too, rotated around the earth.

Nicolaus Copernicus showed that the earth is merely one of a number of heavenly bodies. He observed that the earth rotates and that it also travels around the sun. His observations, his logic, and his mathematics demanded a radical change in the current conception of the heavenly system. He proceeded to make this change.

To explain his theory, Copernicus wrote a remarkable book called *On the Revolutions of the Heavenly Bodies*. He spent a lifetime in writing this book. It was published only a short time before his death. In fact, attendants rushed a copy of the book to his deathbed, and placed his hands upon it.

THE BETTMANN ARCHIVE

Lucky for Copernicus that he was unaware of what a man named Andreas Osiander had secretly written into the front of the volume. Osiander wrote that the thoughts and calculations were merely hypothetical—not to be taken seriously or literally.

Osiander intended in this manner to protect Copernicus from the religious leaders of the day, who resisted any deviation from Ptolemy's geocentric idea of the universe, and could see the earth only as the center of the universe, immobile and dominant. Copernicus, being a scientist, meant what he had written, because that's what he had found.

For the most part, Copernicus presented an accurate picture of the universe. But he erred on one important point. The planets do not travel around the sun in circles, as Copernicus believed. They travel in ellipses, and unless we are strict about this factor, we simply do not get exact answers to many astronomical problems.

Copernicus' fresh approach to the universe was sufficiently earth-shaking to move the earth! His observations took the earth from the erroneous, geocentric position in which Ptolemy had placed it fifteen hundred years earlier to its proper orbit around the sun. Copernicus put the earth where it belongs. This was the extraordinary achievement of the humble, Polish-born scholar.

Today, we can think of the earth as a giant spaceship orbiting around the sun. This spaceship carries its own air, its own water, its own food, and the intelligent beings who endeavor to solve the problems that arise on the huge space liner and who look out into the sky at night. Copernicus, we might say, put us in orbit.

As the earth turns or spins on its axis, it may flatten out a little. Especially would this have happened in the early days of the earth's life, when, presumably, it was hot and plastic. Now, is the earth somewhat flat? Copernicus did not know the actual answer, but we now know the earth is flattened at the poles. It is shorter through the center of the earth from pole to pole than through the equator.

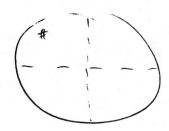

And that's the way it is. Earth is an oblate spheroid. Or almost so. Recent measurements taken by artificial satellites show that it is slightly pear-shaped. It is shaped like a pear that needs a stem!

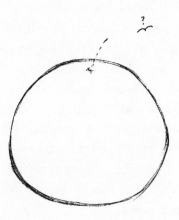

The planet Saturn also is flattened. Saturn spins much faster than does the earth. It makes one turn in 10 hours, 38 minutes, and this faster spinning flattens it out noticeably.

MT. WILSON AND PALOMAR OBSERVATORIES

Jupiter, too, is seen to be rather flattish, making one complete turn in 9 hours, 55 minutes.

MT. WILSON AND PALOMAR OBSERVATORIES

Copernicus, in his study of the solar system, stated that the planet Venus should show phases. There were no telescopes at that time, and with the unaided eye no one could see any phases of Venus, but Copernicus was sure that, if we could only see more clearly, we would discover the phases. In the next century, in 1610, Galileo, looking through a telescope, saw Venus in phase.

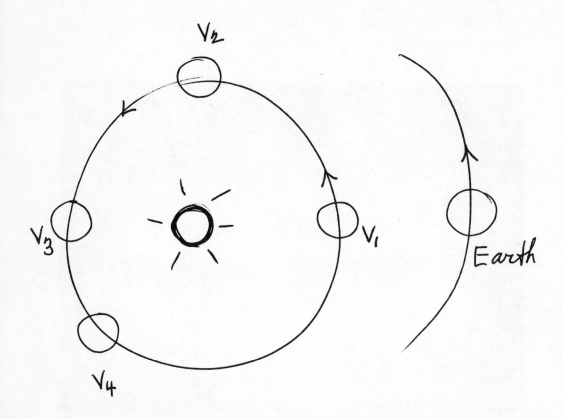

When Venus is at V_1 (see drawing, *above*), we, on earth, should scarcely see it. It is the other side that is receiving the sun. When Venus is at V_3, it is "full", but we have difficulty seeing the full Venus because of the sun's glare. At V_2, on the other hand, we see a half Venus. What do we see at V_4?

Mercury, too, shows phases. But what about Mars, Jupiter, and the other planets on the far side of the earth from the sun? Can you tell about them? Do they show phases?

Hipparchus, you recall, found that the path of the sun around the earth (actually, the path of the earth around the sun) tilted in space as the ages passed? It was Copernicus who saw the explanation of this effect—the earth's axis tips, the precession occurs, and the axis' tip traces a circle.

Even Copernicus did not know the reason for all this. It was Isaac Newton (1642-1727) who explained it all and gave the cause: The sun and the moon tug on the earth's equatorial bulge, causing its axis to tip. How fascinating to consider: Copernicus stood on the shoulders of Hipparchus and saw more clearly into nature than heretofore; and Newton stood on the shoulders of Copernicus, to see more clearly still.

Let us consider in some detail the life of this founder of modern astronomy. He was born in Thorn, in Prussian Poland, and his name in Polish was Koppernigk. In those days, it was the custom to Latinize names, and thus we have Copernicus. His father was a Polish merchant, a trader, who died when Nicolaus was a mere child. His uncle, a Catholic bishop, saw to his education.

Nicolaus went to the University of Cracow in Poland, and studied mathematics with considerable success. Desiring a varied career, he went on to Bologna, Italy, where he studied church law and astronomy. He even studied medicine, at the University of Padua, and became a physician.

Nicolaus then returned to Poland, where, through arrangements made by his uncle, he became a canon of the church, and lived with other clergymen in a clergy house in the town of Frauenburg. Copernicus discharged his church duties, and served the poor people as a doctor, and continued his study of the planets and the stars.

The theories and work of Nicolaus Copernicus paved the way (the Milky Way?) for the telescopic discoveries of Galileo, the planetary laws of Kepler, and the theory of universal gravitation of Newton. Isaac Newton knew what he was saying when he spoke of standing on the shoulders of giants. And, today, earthlings venturing into space know what they are doing. They know because Nicolaus Copernicus once inhabited the mighty spaceship earth.

Tycho

5

Tycho Brahe

1546-1601

Tycho Brahe, at the age of nineteen, suffered the misfortune of having his nose cut off in a duel. He had been arguing about mathematics with a young man named Manderupius when they began insulting each other. Accordingly, the two arranged a duel with swords, and in one wild rush, Manderupius, at one fell swoop, cut off Tycho's nose.

This misfortune neither discouraged nor inhibited Tycho. He made for himself a nose out of gold and silver, using a special cement to keep it in place. For a spare, and to fit in with changing seasons, he also had a nose made of putty and brass. He managed to carry on satisfactorily with his artificial organ, except that once in a while, when he sneezed, his nose would fly off and go tumbling. Tycho, however, always carried his little box of cement with him, and he found it no trouble at all to remedy matters.

Tycho's nose was a great conversation piece in Denmark for many years. But Tycho didn't mind. He was busy with the stars, and he paid scant attention to what others were saying. He simply managed his own affairs, and, you might say, was the one person in the country who, by disposition as well as by circumstance, never put his nose into other people's business.

And it all paid off. Tycho became the greatest observational astronomer who ever lived. What is more, he worked in the days before telescopes were known!

Tycho was a handsome man. With his red hair, blue eyes, reddish moustachio and beard, and a golden nose, he was a colorful figure. A man of great intelligence, perseverance in work, high sense of justice, and consuming interest in the heavens, he was for many years one of the giants among the world's seekers after knowledge.

What really started Tycho on the road of scientific investigation was an event that occurred when he was only a boy of fourteen. He had heard that astronomers had predicted an eclipse of the sun would occur on August 21, 1560. Unfailingly, at the indicated time, the eclipse took place. So stirred was Tycho by this event, so filled with wonder and admiration, that he thereupon decided to become an astronomer.

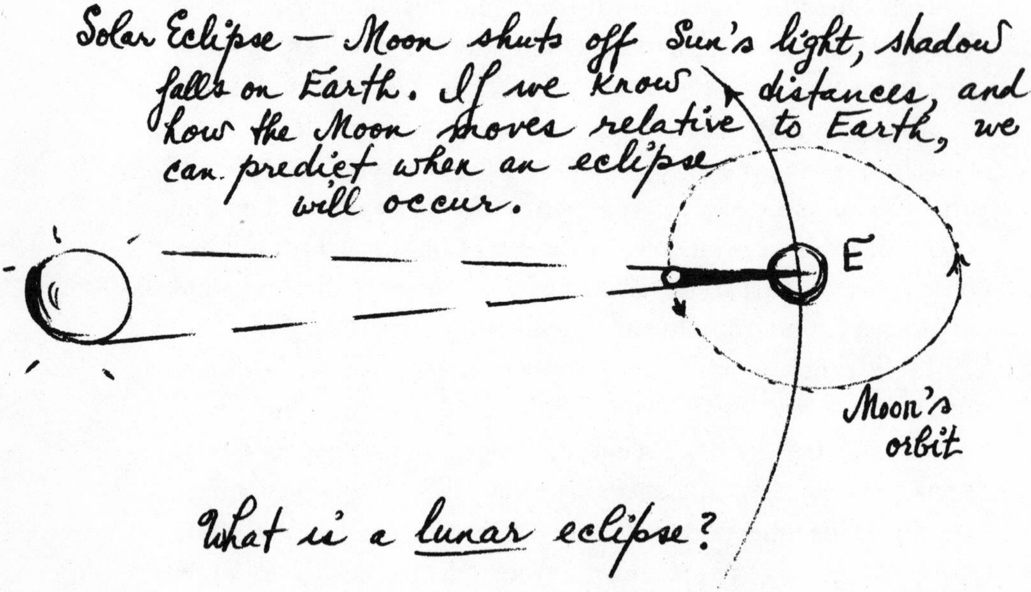

Solar Eclipse — Moon shuts off Sun's light, shadow falls on Earth. If we know distances, and how the Moon moves relative to Earth, we can predict when an eclipse will occur.

Moon's orbit

E

What is a lunar eclipse?

Often a young boy or girl is inspired by some circumstance or event that moves him to decide on his life's work. Albert Einstein, at the age of only four or five, was given a compass. The behavior of the needle in always returning to the self-same position was so startling to him that he thought about it for days. Very likely, this simple event had a lasting effect upon Einstein.

Tycho, in preparing for his career, studied at many places—at Copenhagen, at Leipzig, at Rostock, and at Augsburg.

Once out of the classroom, Tycho lost no time in beginning his life's work. His mother's brother, Steno Belle, had a castle near Knudstrup. He allowed Tycho to install a laboratory and an observatory in the castle.

Tycho started modestly, the first instrument that he constructed being nothing more than a jointed ruler, which had sights for fixing the positions of the planets with respect to the stars. Such simple instruments had been employed centuries earlier by Hipparchus. In time, however, Tycho went on to produce amazingly precise instruments, and some huge, ingenious ones.

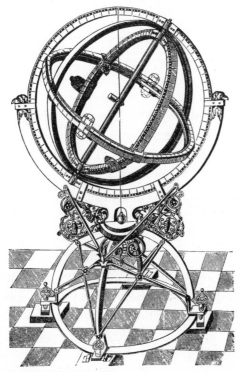

CULVER PICTURES, INC.

To what use would Tycho put an instrument such as this? Also, can you explain how a sextant works?

49

On November 11, 1572, Tycho suddenly saw a "new" star in the constellation of Cassiopeia. It was a marvelous sight—an unexpected, brilliant light shining in the heavens, so luminous that it could be seen even during the daytime. "De Nova Stella," it came to be known, but people soon began calling it "Tycho's Star."

Of course, we know, and Tycho knew, that the star had not actually been born on November 11, 1572. It had not actually come to life at the moment Tycho first observed it. The "new" star had merely flared up. Such a star, however, is still known as a *nova*. Should it blow itself up beyond control and explode for keeps, it would be called, naturally, a *supernova*.

In a nova, we now know, nuclear changes take place which generate so much heat that the entire star expands. As the star expands, however, it cools, and therefore, it subsides, the outer portions settling back under the star's gravitational pull. The star thereupon becomes once again moderate in both size and temperature.

The nuclear reactions that generate the great temporary heat are, in effect, those of fusion. The nuclei of atoms combine with the nuclei of other atoms. As the nuclei fuse, they form a new element, giving off, at the same time, a tremendous amount of heat. Fusion is constantly going on in the sun. There, hydrogen nuclei eventually fuse into helium nuclei.

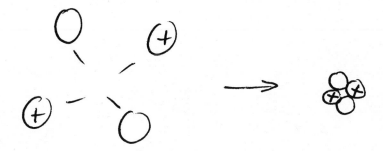

The new nucleus is less in mass than the four single nuclei would lead us to expect. The missing mass becomes radiated energy, such as light, X rays, and gamma rays.

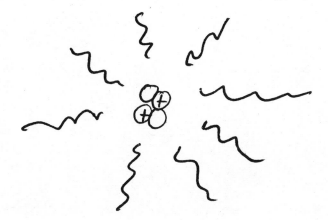

When trillions of such events occur simultaneously, the star suddenly swells and shines out brilliantly.

Tycho's Star remained visible for one and a half years, then gradually faded from sight. Incidentally, in A.D. 1054,

51

Chinese astronomers spotted a new star—a star more spectacular than the one Tycho was to see some five hundred years later. The Chinese star was a supernova, and it really put on a show in the heavens.

In fact, this supernova continues to flare, and as it keeps on exploding and expanding, all heaven breaks loose in the vicinity. In a furious, outward flight, the flaming parts rush away from the center at more than 700 miles per second! This is the *Crab Nebula*.

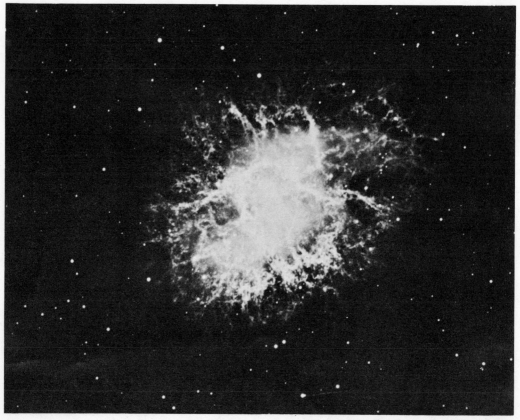

MT. WILSON AND PALOMAR OBSERVATORIES

Tycho attempted to measure the distance of his star from earth, but he could not do it. To understand why he failed, we must have a look at how distances are measured in astronomy.

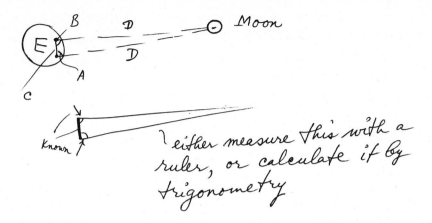

either measure this with a ruler, or calculate it by trigonometry

In the drawing above, C is a base line, say one thousand miles in length. An astronomer at one end measures the angle A, while an astronomer at the other end measures the angle B. Thus, we have a triangle, with one side and two angles known. It is simple, then, to calculate the sides D.

If, however, the object is far, far away, as was *Tycho's Star,* this method fails, because the two angles are each about $90°$. As a result, the lines D and D might be drawn parallel, or almost parallel. This is a defect which occurs simply because of the star's great distance—the angles really are less than $90°$. Hence, we need a larger base line. What do you think of this one?

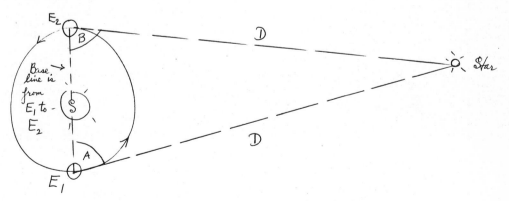

E_1 is earth's position at one time; E_2 is earth's position six months later. Angle A is measured now. Angle B is measured six months later. The base line is $2 \times 93,000,000$, or 186,000,000 miles. Again, knowing the two angles and the length of one side of the triangle, we can easily calculate D.

Even the large base line of the diameter of earth's orbit around the sun becomes too small for measuring star distances which are greater than about 100 light years. (One light year is the *distance* that light travels in one year, or 186,000 miles/second $\times$ 60 seconds/minute $\times$ 60 minutes/hour $\times$ 24 hours/day $\times$ 365 days/year, which comes out to about 6,000,000,000,000 miles, or 6 trillion miles, or 6×10^{12} miles.) We must consider later the methods the astronomers use in the case of these very enormous distances in space.

Tycho, granting that he could not solve the problem of obtaining the distance of his star from earth, remained, however, undaunted. Characteristically, he plunged more ardently into further work. For one thing, Tycho knew that the astronomical tables giving positions of stars and motions of planets were not accurate, so he set about the task of correcting them.

It is only fair to record that Tycho's work was made easier by his devoted wife, a peasant girl whom he married despite his own aristocracy. His relatives were outraged at Tycho's marrying a "common" girl. Tycho ignored them.

His work was made easier also by the fact that King Frederick II of Denmark had given Tycho ample territory on the island of Hveen in the sound on which presently came into being a vast observatory. This, in fact, became the first observatory in history, with operational premises located in the tremendous castle of Uraniborg.

Tycho was receiving a pension here, of 500 thalers per year, and he also had income from an estate in Norway. Under such tolerable conditions, Tycho really settled down at Uraniborg, formally opening the observatory on August 8, 1576.

For twenty-one years Tycho performed his remarkable observations of the heavens with the aid of his own instruments. Here, at the observatory, Tycho was King. He was independent, arrogant with unwanted visitors, busy, and content. His dog, Lep the Oracle, added to his contentment. Tycho, at times, jovially pretended to consult Lep the Oracle on difficult astronomical problems.

THE BETTMANN ARCHIVE

This very dog, indirectly, brought catastrophe to Tycho. The event occurred in a most unexpected way.

One day the Chancellor of Denmark, Walchendorf, came to visit the Observatory of Uraniborg. Tycho, somewhat haughty, showed Walchendorf around, secretly wishing his visitor would stop boring him and would leave him to his work. As they were about to leave one of Tycho's instrument rooms, Lep the Oracle appeared in the doorway and stood looking up at his master, while blocking the passageway. Walchendorf waved at the dog.

"Get out!" he snapped. "Out!"

Lep did not move.

Walchendorf forthwith swung his leg and kicked the animal out of the doorway and into the corridor.

Tycho, livid with rage, turned on the chancellor, declaring him to be a person of mean spirit.

"I don't care who you are!" he shouted. "This is my domain. This is my dog, my noble friend, and you won't dare touch him again!"

Walchendorf left abruptly.

"We'll see," he muttered.

Upon the death of Tycho's sponsor and benefactor, King Frederick II, Christian IV came to power. He was acquainted with Tycho but had little regard for him.

"He is arrogant," said Christian, agreeing with Walchendorf.

Walchendorf was unceasing in his efforts to influence the King against Tycho. Likewise, at court functions, Walchendorf won over his friends and acquaintances to his vendetta against Tycho. Various courtiers were encouraged to incite the King, and even the ordinary people were stirred up by Walchendorf.

One day the King sent a message to Tycho Brahe, supreme astronomer. The message directed Tycho to leave—he was through. The King withdrew the island, the observatory, the pension, and all of Tycho's incomes that he controlled.

Tycho packed up his instruments and left for Rostock, in June of 1599. The Emperor Rudolph II of Prague welcomed this eminent scientist, allotted him the castle of Benatky, and granted him a pension of 3,000 florins per year.

In this castle, the following year, a promising, hardworking astronomer joined Tycho as an assistant. This assistant's name was Johannes Kepler.

Tycho, arrogant, brilliant, industrious, died at Benatky on October 24, 1601, aged 57.

Johannes Kepler took over.

The saddened and devoted Kepler put Tycho's papers in order and finished some of the calculations.

Tycho's principal published work consisted of two volumes, which came out in Prague in 1602 and 1603. The work was edited by Johannes Kepler. The first book gave an exhaustive study of the motions of the sun and moon. In it also were noted the positions of 777 fixed stars. (Years later, in 1627, Kepler boosted the total to 1,005 stars in the publication honoring the king who had befriended Tycho. Kepler called the work *Rudolphine Tables.*)

The second book of Tycho's main work actually had first been privately published at Uraniborg in 1588. It dealt principally with the comet of 1577, the visitor from another world which Tycho had welcomed with jubilation, and the journey of which he had charted with great exactitude. Tycho, in attempting to measure the comet's distance, concluded that it certainly had come from a far away point. It was not, he said, some luminous gas emitted by the earth, as certain observers believed. The comet, Tycho knew, had crossed the distant regions of the planets.

Although Tycho's observational work was magnificent, his theoretical conceptions left much to be desired. He made some mistakes for which there really was no excuse. For example, Copernicus had shown that the sun was dominant and that all the planets traveled around it. Yet, Tycho reverted to Ptolemy, to some extent. He simply did not feel that he could make the earth travel.

Tycho wanted a middle ground (or a middle heaven?) between the systems of Ptolemy and Nicolaus Copernicus. Earth was to be immobile. Yet the other planets were to go around the sun. Tycho, it appeared, wanted to eat his astronomical cake and have it, too.

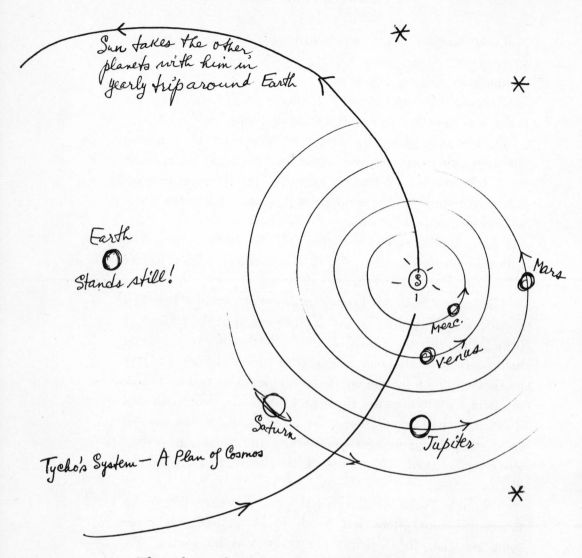

Sun takes the other planets with him in yearly trip around Earth

Earth
◯
Stands still!

Merc.

Venus

Mars

Saturn

Jupiter

Tycho's System — A Plan of Cosmos

The sphere of stars, Tycho declared, must perform a daily rotation around earth! This was monstrously illogical. Yet, whenever he dealt with instruments, and observations, he was incomparable.

Tycho published a fine work on his instruments, and another on the moon's subtle motions. He prepared a most valuable table of refractions, and took into account the errors that instruments themselves are responsible for, and he demonstrated how one should average out accidental errors.

Tycho Brahe worked incessantly. He not only undertook his own projects but also corrected the observations of others. He did all this so that astronomy might become a beautiful and precise science. It did.

On his death bed, Tycho whispered, "Oh, that it may not appear that I have lived in vain!"

He had not lived in vain. None of them have lived in vain. Tycho Brahe advanced the cause of science and of reason. He encouraged the promising Kepler. He will always be remembered.

Take a look at a map of the moon.

There is a beautiful crater there called "Tycho."

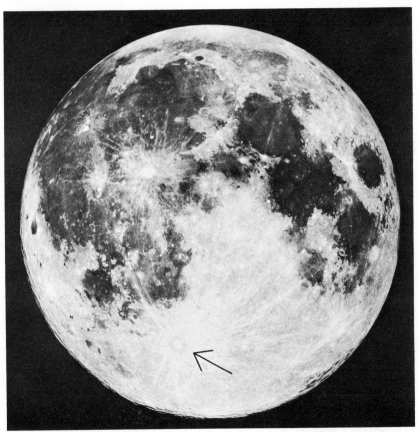

MT. WILSON AND PALOMAR OBSERVATORIES

Kepler

Johannes Kepler

1571-1630

Johannes Kepler, who took over the work of the great observatory when his friend, Tycho Brahe, died, was not an expert observational astronomer. He lacked skill in the use of instruments, nor did he have the physical strength and the temperament necessary to observe carefully, for long hours.

He was, however, outstanding in mathematics, and of superior mind in analysis, speculation, and theorizing. He could study great quantities of numbers—all the data of astronomy relating to the positions and movements of the heavenly bodies—and find relations between the numbers, and evolve order, and write equations, and analyze curves.

We remember Johannes Kepler chiefly for his three laws of planetary motion. Here they are:

1. The planets travel in *elliptical* orbits around the sun; the sun is at one focus.

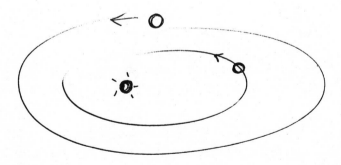

The important point here is that the curve is an *ellipse*, and not a circle, as everyone until Kepler's time had supposed. You will remember that we considered the ellipse previously when appraising Archimedes and his work. At that time, however, we did not claim that Archimedes knew that the planets had elliptical orbits. He knew merely of ellipses, among other curves, as mathematical curves of beauty.

Kepler, after analyzing masses of numbers giving the positions of the planets over a period of many years, was able to state that for some of the planets the ellipse differed very little from a circle, whereas for others the ellipse is very much off center, or *eccentric*. For earth, the eccentricity is not very great.

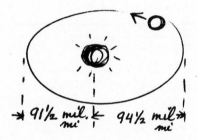

(Sometimes people forget that in the northern hemisphere we earthlings have winter when our planet is closer to the sun than at other times of the year. We have summer when the earth is farther from the sun than at other times. Can you explain why this is so?)

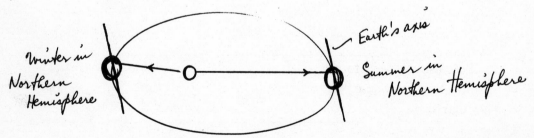

When satellites are launched artificially, they always go into elliptical orbits around the earth, or elliptical orbits around the sun, if they are launched around it. Only a perfect shot could hope to put an artificial satellite into a circular orbit. To achieve a circular shot, the firing speed at a fixed height above the earth would have to be precisely one certain value, and the satellite would have to be fired precisely in a predetermined direction, parallel to the plane of the earth's horizon below.

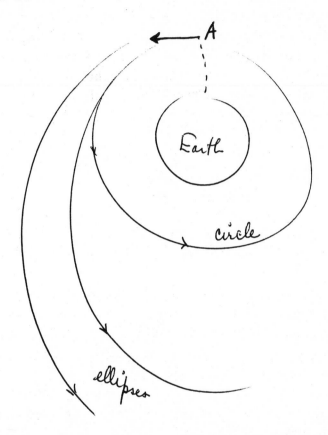

Suppose we were to put an artificial satellite into a circular orbit. Now, suppose we were to try a second time for a circular orbit. If the launching speed were greater than that at A, we would get an ellipse—not a circle. Or, if the direction differed slightly, we would get an ellipse.

Kepler's second law of planetary motion is this:

2. A planet, moving in its elliptical orbit around the sun, proceeds in such a way that the *area* swept out by an

imaginary line connecting the planet to the sun is always the same in a given amount of time, no matter where the planet is.

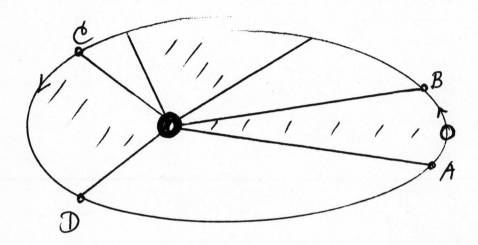

A planet moves from A to B in say two months, and from C to D in two months. The shaded areas are equal—the same number of square miles. Or, we can take a two-month arc anywhere else and draw those lines. The area again will be the same. The lines are called "radius vectors."

What must we conclude from this? It is quite clear that the planet must be moving more rapidly at the C to D region than at the A to B region. Otherwise, how could it happen that the shallow arc from C to D is large enough to make the two areas come out the same?

For earth, then, the speed in orbit is greatest when earth is closest to the sun—in wintertime for the northern hemisphere. Many of us perhaps are glad that earth is apparently in a hurry to escape winter. Earth, then, is dilly-dallying when it is farthest from the sun, in summertime for the northern hemisphere.

In any case, earth certainly speeds up and slows down as it courses through the heavens around the lordly sun.

You can, in a way, copy earth's motion by an experiment, especially if you have a piano. Actually, you don't need the piano—it is the rotating stool you need. You sit on the stool, holding a book out in one hand, while someone gives you a start to set you revolving. Then, as you go round, pull your arm in toward your chest. See how you speed up!

If you feel somewhat off balance with only one book, hold a book in each hand.

Kepler's third law records in a precise way how long a planet takes to go around the sun. The length of time depends on how far away the planet is from the sun. The distant planets take longer than the nearer ones. For example, Mercury, the closest planet to the sun, gets around once in eighty-eight days, but Uranus, much farther, takes eighty-four years!

(Incidentally, it is easy to remember those eighty-four years for Uranus. The man who discovered Uranus, William Herschel (1738-1822), lived to be eighty-four years old— just once around. Had he been living on Uranus, he would have died at the age of one. What an amazing amount of wonderful astronomical work he accomplished for a being who lived to be only one year old!)

Kepler gave the actual mathematical relationship between the time a planet takes to orbit the sun once (the "period") and the distance of the planet from the sun.

Here is the third law:

3. The *squares* of the periods of two planets are in the same ratio as the *cube* of the distance of the first planet to the cube of the distance of the second planet.

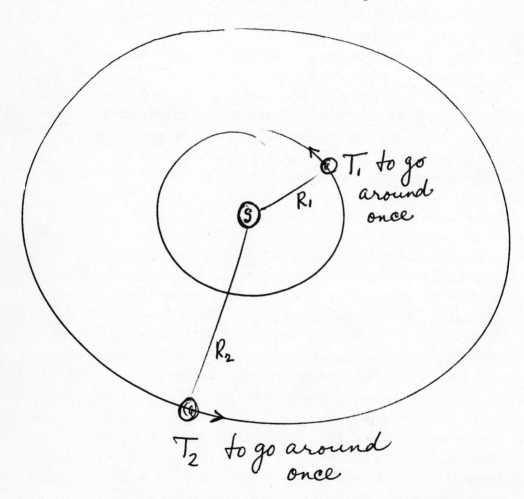

In the diagram, *above,* R_1 and R_2 denote the distances of the planets from the sun. T_1 and T_2 represent the periods. Of course, here Kepler has to take a sort of average R because

66

the planets actually move in ellipses and not in circles. But
the ratio holds true:

$$\frac{T_1{}^2}{T_2{}^2} = \frac{R_1{}^3}{R_2{}^3}$$

But Kepler did not know why! He did not know why the
planets moved in such a way that the ratio held true. And
he did not know why the planets moved in elliptical orbits
rather than in circular ones. He did not know why the law
about areas held true.

Why? What was the *cause* of all this? Was there a cause?

We shall see later who found the cause.

Even without knowing the explanations, Kepler found out
precisely how the planets behaved, how they moved, at which
speeds, and in what sorts of orbits. Imagine the exultation,
the soaring of spirit, a man must feel upon discovering something new about nature and the universe. It took Kepler all
his life, but the joy was forever his when those three laws
stood before his vision.

Yet, how he suffered all his life.

Born at Weil, Wurttemberg, in Germany, Johannes was
the oldest son of a rather reckless, irresponsible father and
a somewhat unstable and poorly educated mother. Neither
the father, who for a while worked as a tavern keeper, nor
his mother, who became involved in a series of scrapes,
really did much for the boy, and it is practically a miracle
that the world ever came to know the great scientist Johannes
Kepler.

To add to his poor environment, fate inflicted a severe
case of smallpox upon the little Johannes when he was three
years old, and the disease left him with poor eyesight and
crippled hands. Thereafter, all his life Johannes had a rather
weak constitution. But he had a wonderful mind.

Somehow, Kepler began to study for a religious career.
But he also delved into the works of Copernicus. He excelled
in astronomy at the University of Tubingen. Upon gradua-

tion, he was offered a teaching position at a Lutheran school in Gratz. At Gratz, Kepler married a rich woman.

There were serious religious disturbances in Germany at the time, and Kepler left Gratz for Prague, where, as we have seen, he became an assistant to Tycho Brahe. Upon the death of the colorful and capable Tycho Brahe, Kepler took over. Emperor Rudolph II made him the imperial mathematician and supported his astronomical projects, but he also expected Kepler to supply him with favorable horoscopes. Although this obligation annoyed him, Kepler complied with the royal expectations.

The young Kepler was amazed yet unabashed upon discovering that as an astronomer he was expected to occupy himself with astrology. Many important people in those days expected astronomers to work out horoscopes for them, and to tell what the stars were planning for them. Kepler had to go along with this trend, and, regrettably enough, he soon began to work out star predictions even for himself. He kept a daily record of his personal experiences along with notations on the stars and planets.

This sort of activity led him to believe that he had found some mysterious power which determined the number of the planets and their distances. He felt sure, for a long time, that the shapes of some geometrical bodies—the five regular solids—had a connection with the disposition and number of the planets. Of course, all of these extraordinary notions were discredited with the discovery of other planets.

On September 30, 1604, a wonderful event took place. Kepler saw a new star! Tycho had seen one, and here was his successor, Johannes Kepler, also discovering a nova. Perhaps there was something to that notion of the secret plans of the stars.

Tycho's Star had remained visible for eighteen months. Kepler's star followed suit almost exactly, remaining visible for seventeen months before fading away.

Kepler studied the planet Mars with especial attention, because it has a rather eccentric orbit.

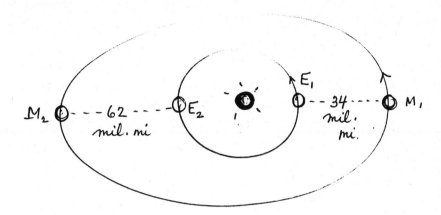

At the closest, earth and Mars are about thirty-four million miles apart. At their other positions, shown above, the two planets are more than sixty million miles apart.

You remember that earth's orbit is not very eccentric, its distances from the sun being $91\frac{1}{2}$ and $94\frac{1}{2}$ million miles. Hence, Mars is in quite an eccentric orbit.

Kepler also made progress in attempting to understand the tides produced on earth. He said that the moon was responsible, and he talked about gravity. Yet, in science, a qualitative statement often means little. It took Newton really to formulate a *mathematical* theory of the tides, and to give teeth to speculations about gravity. Still, Kepler's intuition and insight were good.

In 1610 came a great event. Kepler received a telescope for the first time. Thereafter, he could scarcely tear himself from the skies.

However, the friendly Emperor Rudolph, benefactor of both Tycho and Kepler, was driven from the Bohemian throne by his own brother, Matthias, in 1611. Thus, once again there were complications in the life of Johannes Kepler. He had expected to receive a considerable sum of money due him as back salary, but, now with Rudolph gone, the prospect suddenly dimmed.

Still, Kepler worked on, pay or no pay. His wife died in 1611, and a few years later he married again, this time an orphan girl.

He studied comets and the motions of the moon. He tried to divine the secrets of the entire universe with a mixture of intuition and mathematics. But he didn't quite manage it.

Again there were cruel distractions. Authorities charged Kepler's mother with being a witch, and she was arrested. Almost anyone could get into trouble in those days upon being accused of some imagined sorcery by an enemy or by some hysterical person. Kepler left his work and rushed to his mother's assistance in another city, and after exhausting himself with the effort, he finally got her out of prison.

The poor woman, however, had spent thirteen months in jail, badgered, abused, and threatened with torture, while demands were made that she confess that she was a witch. How this poor, brave woman withstood the brutality and cruelty is difficult to imagine. Unfortunately, her vicious accusers—the sadists and tyrants—did take their toll. Several months after her release the mother of one of the greatest men of science who ever lived died—beaten, exhausted.

Kepler turned back to his work, compiling tables about the stars and planets, publishing catalogues with mathematical calculations, and predicting the passage of Mercury and Venus across the face of the sun. He also spent much time "proving" that the distances of the planets were related to musical intervals, and he believed this to be true, even at the height of his genuinely scientific accomplishment.

His salary seldom was paid on time, or in full, and driven by sheer necessity to obtain some money, he set out one day in November of 1630 on a long journey to Prague, where, before the Emperor's court, he humbled himself and begged for the money due him. He failed to get the money.

70

The journey had been difficult, exhausting. He fell sick with fever. Anguished, the poverty stricken astronomer lay spiritless. This was the man who had found the planetary laws, the man who, at the moment the heavenly mysteries stood revealed, had written:

. . . that for which I joined Tycho Brahe, for which I settled down in Prague, for which I have devoted the best part of my life to astronomical meditations, at length I have brought to light, and recognized its truth beyond my most sanguine expectations. It is not quite eighteen months since I got the first glimpse of light, three months since the dawn, very few days since the unveiled sun, most admirable to gaze upon, burst upon me. Nothing holds me; I will indulge my sacred fury; I will triumph over mankind by the honest confession that I have stolen the golden vases of the Egyptians to build a tabernacle for my God far away from the confines of Egypt. If you forgive me, I rejoice; if you are angry, I can bear it; the die is cast, the book is written, to be read either now or by posterity, I care not which; it may well wait a century for a reader, as God has waited six thousand years for an observer.

He had come for his money, so that he might live, and work. He didn't get it. He lay sick. On November 15, 1630, Johannes Kepler died.

Galileo

SCRIPTA MATHEMATICA

7

Galileo Galilei

1564-1642

Everybody knows the story of Galileo's going up onto the Leaning Tower of Pisa, from where he dropped simultaneously a heavy metallic ball and a light one.

BETTMANN

What happened? The two objects reached the ground at the same time. Yet, the great and inviolate Aristotle had written that, the heavier the object, the faster it falls.

Had Aristotle tried the experiment himself? Not likely. He might have dropped a feather and a rock, and might have seen the rock reach the ground first, because the air would have interfered with the fall of the feather.

Nowadays we can drop a feather and a rock in a tube from which the air has been removed, and see them land at the same time.

The men around Galileo, for the most part, rejected new ideas. Other professors and students at the University of Pisa believed too strongly in the authority of Aristotle to accept Galileo's observation about falling bodies. Moreover, to them, Galileo was an upstart. What would he do next?

Galileo believed in the scientific way of finding out things: Experiment, then think about results and try to come up with a law or a principle. Then do more experiments to test out your theoretical ideas. If you can't confirm these ideas, you had better rethink. Get a new principle, if possible, then check it by experiment. Continue in this way until a satisfactory and undeniable conclusion has been reached. Galileo was the "Father of the Scientific Method."

This new method caused him a great deal of trouble.

He was born in this very same town of Pisa, where his father, though far from rich, was a well-known dealer in cloth. The father was a capable musician and mathematician. He hoped that Galileo, the eldest of seven children, would become a doctor, rather than try for pure science. A career in medicine, the father knew, would pay well, compared with the meager earnings of a scientist in those days.

The young Galileo, like his father, was talented in music. As a youth, he also excelled in painting. But, upon enrolling in the University of Pisa, he discovered mathematics. Science and mathematics simply reached out to him, as had no other interest in the past. The father threw up his hands, and sighed, "All right, go to it. But you'll starve."

It was in his first year at the university that the event of the swinging lamp occurred. Galileo had gone one morning to the cathedral at Pisa, when, suddenly, he became fascinated by the swinging lamp. Galileo observed that it seemed to take the same amount of time to make a complete oscillation even when the arc became increasingly smaller as time passed.

Galileo timed the swings with his pulse, and in this way, he verified his observation. Actually, today we know that, if the arc is unusually large, the time is not the same as for a small arc. But you can certainly say that the time is very nearly the same. It is almost perfectly identical if the angles are less than about 10°.

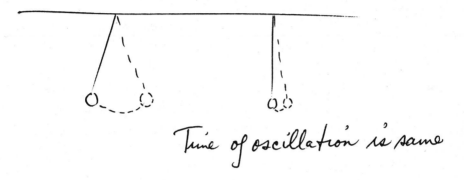

Time of oscillation is same

Galileo found that the material of the bob has no effect on the timing, nor does the weight. What matters is the *length* of the pendulum. A long pendulum beats more slowly than a short one. A pendulum four times as long as another takes two times as long to make a beat.

Galileo figured out how to make such a constant-time pendulum activate some gears in order to produce a clock. About fifteen years later Christian Huygens (1629-1695) followed through with these ideas and made the first successful pendulum clock, such as we use even today.

In working with his pendulum, Galileo used it to measure a person's pulse. Thus, he made a valuable medical instrument, even though he was really on his way to pure science and had turned away from a career in medicine.

Galileo ran out of money and had to leave the university, but his scientific work went on, even more intensely than before. He appeared at numerous scientific gatherings to report on his findings. Everyone could see that here was a gifted young man, and some scientists began to call him "the Archimedes of our time."

Upon leaving his classes, Galileo could not at first find work. In fact, it was four years before he really settled down. Then, he returned to his very own university, not as a student but as a teacher. He accepted a humble post as lecturer in mathematics. Along with his teaching he began to look closely into many problems that had interested him.

For several years, he investigated the motion of falling bodies, until the climax of the leaning-tower demonstration which earned him a lot of enemies. He didn't help himself any when he ridiculed university regulations and conformity, and soon he found that he could do nothing but resign.

He obtained a new position at the University of Padua, where he remained for eighteen years, and produced an amazing amount of original scientific work. His work on the motion of bodies was extremely thorough, and opened up an entirely new branch of physics—mechanics.

Here are a few of the ideas that he worked out, through a combination of experiment and abstract reasoning—through the scientific method:

1. Suppose an object travels at a uniform velocity from one point to another.

From this event, Galileo concluded:

$$S = v \times t$$

where S is the distance, v is the velocity, and t is the total time of the journey.

2. An object, however, may accelerate, where "acceleration" means the rate of change of velocity, or

$$a = \frac{V_2 - V_1}{t}$$

where a is the acceleration, V_1 is the first velocity, V_2 is the new velocity, and t is the time that elapses as the velocity changes from V_1 to V_2.

3. If an object falls straight down toward earth, it goes a distance S, in a time t, and

$$S = \tfrac{1}{2}gt^2$$

where g is the special acceleration that occurs for falling bodies. As you know, g is 32 feet per second every second. That is, the velocity changes by 32 feet per second every second.

4. The bodies shown below all have the same speed when they reach the bottom. Can you explain this?

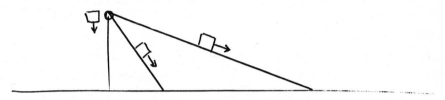

5. A projectile fired from earth traces a parabola in space. (Strictly speaking, it is a part of an ellipse, but if we neglect the curvature of the earth, the parabola is all right.)

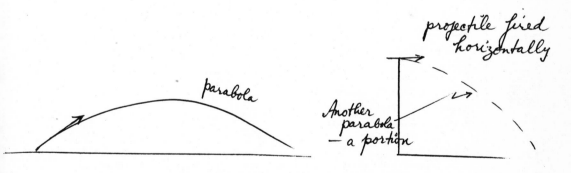

parabola

Another parabola — a portion

projectile fired horizontally

6. The best angle, for the biggest range, is 45°.

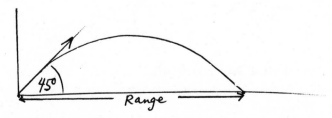

45°

Range

Any other angle with the same projectile velocity will give a lesser range.

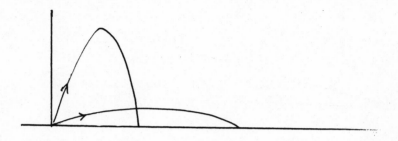

It can be shown that, with the same initial projectile speed, you can aim at two different angles and still hit the same spot on the ground—if you select the right angles, that is.

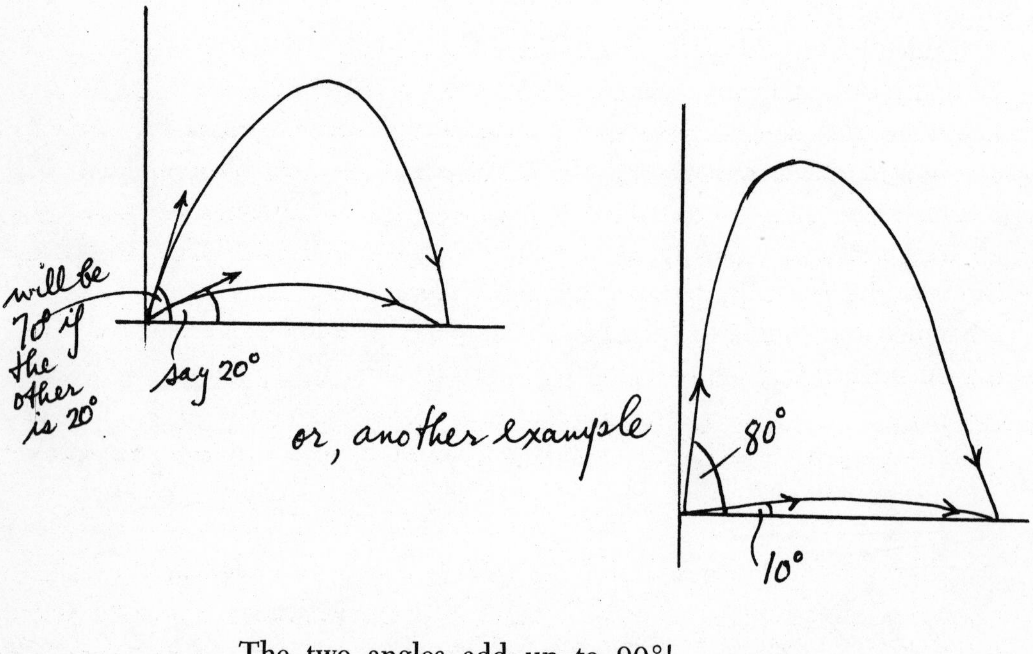

will be 70° if the other is 20°

say 20°

or, another example

80°

10°

The two angles add up to 90°!

Try this with a water hose on your front lawn. You will see that it works.

Galileo also figured out how velocities add up, if an object is urged in more than one direction at the same time.

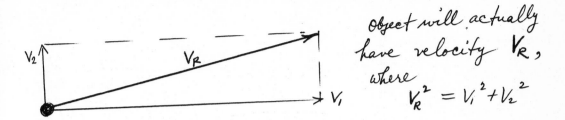

object will actually have velocity V_R, where

$$V_R^2 = V_1^2 + V_2^2$$

In the year 1609, Galileo heard that some Dutch technicians were beginning to produce magnifying glasses. There was a report, too, that a Dutch boy had actually put several lenses together and produced an amazing device. By looking through the lenses, one could see an object three times as big as it would normally appear. The object, however, was seen upside down!

Galileo labored through the night on a theory. By dawn, he had it—the telescope. He made a telescope forthwith. The object he viewed was right side up, because Galileo figured out how to make it come up right.

Breathless with this turn of events, he rushed out to look at the moon. Mountains and craters he saw! He stared through the night in fascination.

Galileo soon made a telescope of a magnifying power of 32. A single lens would form an image, as shown.

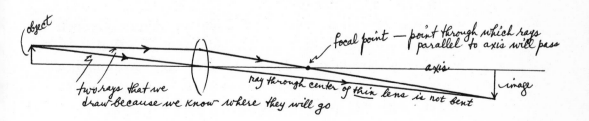

object

focal point — point through which rays parallel to axis will pass

axis

image

two rays that we draw because we know where they will go

ray through center of thin lens is not bent

If, however, we interpose an eyepiece of this type ![diverging lens symbol],
a diverging type, we get an upright image. (This is called
"virtual," because the light is not really there.)

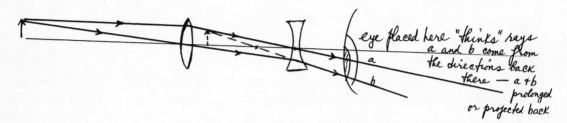

eye placed here "thinks" rays
a and b come from
the directions back
there — a + b
prolonged
or projected back

The telescope revealed to Galileo four moons of Jupiter.
This observation was like the discovery of a new world. Today, we know that Jupiter has twelve moons. Some of them
are bigger than our moon.

Galileo also saw Venus in phase, just as Copernicus had
led astronomers to expect. This event certainly put the
clincher on Copernicus' heavenly system, in which the planets
all travel around the sun.

Galileo also had some long looks at Saturn through
his telescope. He couldn't quite decide what it was that he
was seeing. He did not distinguish the rings, because they
were approximately edge-on at that time. His telescopic
power really was not very high.

"It is triple," Galileo wrote, mistaking end portions of the
edge-on rings for two moons.

During the day he covered the front end of the objective lens with a darkened glass to shut out most of the sunlight. With his eyes protected, he studied the sun. He was amazed to see sunspots.

Some of the sunspots are huge. I measured one that was 90,000 miles in diameter. We know now that these spots are areas of electrical and magnetic storms. Galileo wondered about them, gaping in awe and joy at the same time.

Galileo made hundreds of telescopes with his own hands. They found their way to scholars all over Europe. Meanwhile, his unending studies of the heavens revealed many stars never before seen by the eyes of men. He also observed nebulae, though he could not quite divine their meaning.

Galileo predicted that someday planets would be known beyond Saturn, and, of course, we now have found Uranus, Neptune, and Pluto. There is reason to expect that beyond Pluto are still other planets belonging to our sun, and countless planets belonging to other suns—stars, that is.

Galileo explored the Milky Way. It was no hazy cloud. It was a heavenly sea of stars! Men on Planet Earth were beginning to get glimpses of the universe. All this was enough to flood a man's soul with reverence and amazement, and with the ecstasy of revelation.

Each night seemed to bring a new discovery. He now was sure that Copernicus had been right.

"All my life and being from now on depend upon having men accept the insight of Copernicus," he affirmed.

Galileo began to have troubles. He tried to show that the theory of Copernicus was compatible with the Scriptures. Certain theological philosophers, however, attacked him. He replied by saying, "The Bible shows how to go to heaven, not how heaven goes."

But this comment only served to get him into deeper water.

There is a long story of Galileo's chastisement: how he was admonished to leave the earth immobile and not put it traveling about the sun; how he tried to win friends among the theological hierarchy, and how he succeeded for a time, only to be accused of slipping back to his previous stand; how he was finally brought before the Inquisition and forced to sign a statement denying his beliefs about the earth's behavior in the heavens.

Broken in health and humiliated, Galileo was forced to remain secluded in certain areas. He could travel or change his abode only by permission. Only a few friends were permitted to visit him, along with his daughter, who suffered grievously because of her father's ordeal. She did everything that she could for him. Neglecting herself, she became ill and died.

Galileo became blind. He still carried on his scientific work by dictating to one or two loyal friends.

One brief bright moment was the visit of the poet John Milton, who sat entranced as he listened to the old blind man speak of the universe. The opportunity to gaze through Galileo's telescopes delighted Milton. Some twenty-five years later the great poet himself became blind. But he too carried on with his work—he dictated *Paradise Lost* to his daughters.

Galileo dictated his scientific thoughts to the very end. It was on January 8, 1642, that his voice was stilled.

But not his writings. They speak as loudly now as in his own day.

He had brought mathematical analysis to physical problems; he had perfected the science of mechanics; he had discovered a new universe with the telescope that he had built; he had studied subtle motions of the moon; and he had explained that the light on the new moon is caused by earth shine.

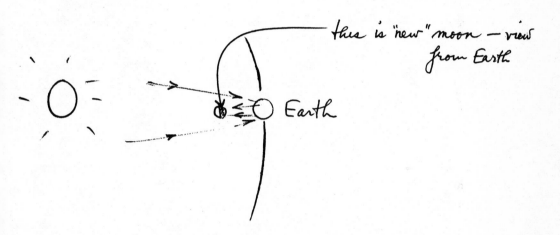

this is "new" moon — view from Earth

Earth

True, Galileo did not quite grasp the idea of relating force and motion, contenting himself largely with a description of motions themselves. Although he spoke of gravity, he did not hit upon the notion of a universal force of gravitation—the notion that any two objects in the universe attract each other, and in a very special way that can be represented mathematically.

Yes, all this is true. But, in the very year of his death, a boy was born in England who was to stand eventually on Galileo's shoulders and reach higher still into the unknown heavens, and pluck from them the secrets of force and planetary motion, and extract the law of universal gravitation.

Huygens

8

Christian Huygens

1629-1695

In the year 1665, this puzzle appeared in a Dutch magazine:

aaaaaaa	nnnnnnnnn
cccc	oooo
d	pp
eeeee	q rr s
g h	
iiiiiii	tttt
llll mm	uuuuu

That's all there was, except for a name below it: Christian Huygens.

This name, however, meant a great deal.

Christian Huygens was a great scientist. He was the son of Constantijn, Holland's greatest classical poet, a friend of the famous, a bon vivant and an attractive personage.

Those who read the magazine understood the puzzle to some extent. At least they readily understood why Huygens had placed it in the periodical. He was making a claim.

Christian Huygens had made a discovery. He wanted to publicize his findings in code. But he wanted to say nothing more about the discovery until it was made known to people everywhere. Then he would reveal the meaning of his code, or puzzle.

If Huygens had clearly set forth his discovery in a professional journal, word would have gotten around quickly, and someone else would have rushed into print in his own locality, claiming that he had discovered whatever it was. In those days, published communication spread very slowly.

Soon, Christian felt safe in his claim. He then revealed what the puzzle meant. The letters made up the following sentence:

"Annulo cingitur, tenui, plano, nunquam cohaerente, ad eclipticam inclinato."

As far as most of us are concerned, it would be still a puzzle. Many people in the days of Christian Huygens, however, knew that the sentence meant:

"It is girdled by a thin flat ring, nowhere touching, inclined to the ecliptic."

What was girdled?

Christian was telling the world that Saturn had a ring!

This was unheard of. A planet with a ring around it?

Galileo had looked at Saturn with a telescope, and had noted no ring. True, Galileo had seen something. But he took the fuzzy appearances to be moons.

How was it that Christian could see a ring?

Soon, it all became clear. Saturn's ring system sometimes presented itself edge-on toward earth, and at that time the rings could scarcely be seen. Sometimes the ring system presented itself more or less in a broadside manner. The rings then were a beautiful sight—shining, wide, easily perceivable even through a small telescope.

The photographs obtainable today not only show the ring system clearly, but also show how the view from earth changes about every seven years. When earth happens to be at A and Saturn at A_1 (see diagram, page 87), the rings are edge-on to earthlings. When earth happens to be at D and Saturn at D_1 (about six or seven years later), the rings are seen "full" to earthlings.

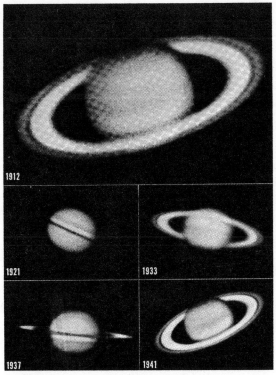

LOWELL OBSERVATORY, FLAGSTAFF, ARIZONA;
PHOTOS BY E. C. SLIPHER

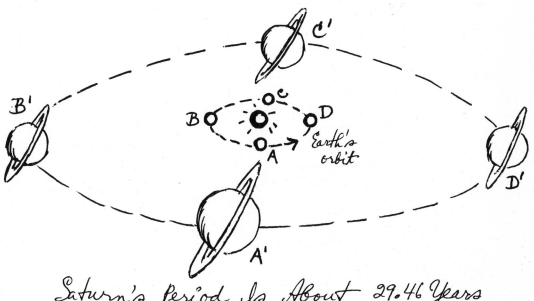

Saturn's Period Is About 29.46 Years

In 1675, G. D. Cassini found a black gap dividing the ring into two concentric rings. We now know that there are at least three distinct bands, or rings.

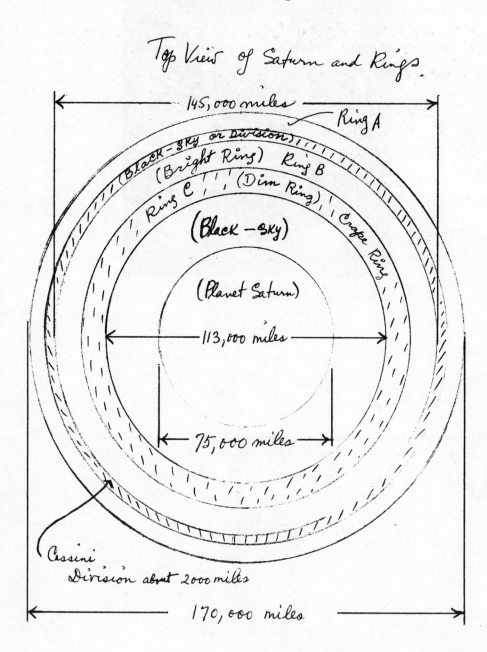

Top View of Saturn and Rings.

145,000 miles — Ring A

(Black-Sky or Division)

(Bright Ring) Ring B

Ring C (Dim Ring)

Crape Ring

(Black-Sky)

(Planet Saturn)

113,000 miles

75,000 miles

Cassini Division about 2000 miles

170,000 miles

In the eighteenth century, another Cassini, Jacques, suggested that the rings were made up of particles. In 1857, James Clerk Maxwell proved mathematically that the rings could not be solid. If they were solid, they would break up under Saturn's gravitational pull, unless the solid material of the rings was distributed in a very unusual and uneven manner. This was such an unlikely possibility, however, that Maxwell ruled it out as a practical happenstance. His essay on this subject, titled "On the Stability of Motion of Saturn's Rings," won Maxwell the famous Adams prize at the University of Cambridge.

In 1895, the astronomer Keeler proved experimentally what Jacques Cassini had guessed and what Maxwell had proven on paper by mathematics. The rings, Keeler observed, were indeed made up of tiny, discrete particles. The inner portion of a ring, he observed, moved faster than the outer portion. If a ring were solid, like a wheel, then the outer portion would move faster than the inner portion. But, with a ring of Saturn, the opposite was true.

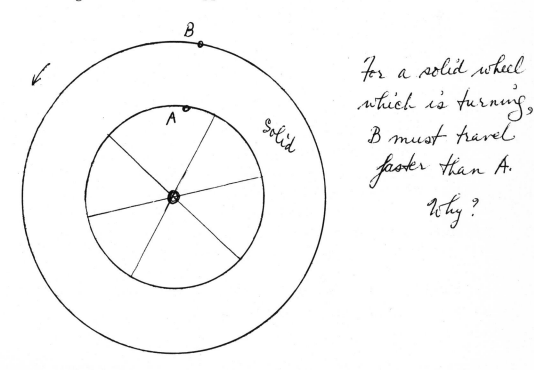

For a solid wheel which is turning, B must travel faster than A.

Why?

A tiny satellite like one of the particles within a ring of Saturn moves faster at a point close to the planet than at a point away from the planet. This, of course, is also true of a big satellite. Artificial satellites whirling around earth have speeds of something like 18,000 mph, whereas the very distant moon travels around the earth at only about 2,000 mph.

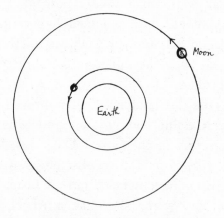

Some astronomers believe that the particles of the rings are billions of tiny ice crystals. Others theorize that the particles are finer than ice crystals. The rings A and C are transparent. This we know because one of Saturn's moons has been seen by the astronomer Barnard right through the inner ring (called "crape"). The moon was only dimly visible through this ring. Yet, it *was* visible. Several other astronomers have observed the outer ring pass over a star, and the star was not completely hidden from view.

As to the origin of the rings, we cannot say too much with any degree of certainty. Could they have come into being when one of Saturn's moons exploded? Or, is Saturn merely a planet in its early stage of development? Perhaps all planets at first have rings that slowly coalesce into moons. Or did Saturn itself, long ago, explode equatorially in a series of bursts, spewing out its matter in a whirling action. After all, Saturn turns very rapidly on its axis, you will recall.

In the years ahead, the rings will present themselves in this way to earthlings: in 1965, edge-on; 1972, open; and 1979, edge-on. The rings moved into an open position in 1958.

When the rings are open, the light from Saturn is of course far greater than at other times, and the sight is perhaps the most beautiful of all in the heavens.

About that "ad eclipticam inclinato": the plane of the rings is inclined at 28° to the earth's orbit around the sun, or the ecliptic; about 27° to Saturn's orbit. With this information in mind, what can you conclude about the planes of the orbits of Saturn and earth?

So it was Christian Huygens who started us studying the rings of Saturn. Then all the theoretical and observational scientists—physicists, mathematicians, astronomers—set about elucidating this delightful wonder of nature. Work still remains. Other men will build further, and eventually we will have the final answer to the puzzle of Saturn's rings.

You would think that for one man the accomplishment of discovering Saturn's rings might be enough. There is, however, more glory associated with the name of Christian Huygens.

Huygens was fortunate. He came from a privileged home. His father, besides being a great poet, served as Secretary of State for three successive Princes of Orange in Holland.

Constantijn, the father, visited England. He became a good friend of John Donne, whose poetry he translated for the Dutch people. A passage from one of Donne's *Devotions* made a deep impression on Constantijn, and very probably, Christian, too:

No man is an Iland, intire of it selfe; every man is a peece of the Continent, a part of the maine; if a Clod bee washed away by the Sea, Europe is the lesse, as well as if a Promontorie were, as well as if a Manor of thy friends or of thine owne were. Any mans death diminishes me, because I am involved in Mankinde. And therefore never send to know for whom the bell tolls; it tolls for thee.

Constantijn was a Latin scholar, a musician, and a mathematician. He it was who tutored Christian, particularly in mathematics. Christian, as a boy, studied languages intensively. He also worked hard at his drawing and music. In mechanics and mathematics he was already unusually competent at the age of thirteen.

A career for him, at first, seemed to be law. He began his law studies at Leyden. At the age of seventeen, however, he sent his first mathematical paper to Professor Marsenne, who was amazed by the youth's work. The professor called young Huygens "The Dutch Archimedes."

From then on, Christian fairly burst upon the scientific world, with his studies of the theory of probability and the cross section of a cone, and, with his elder brother, astronomy. The two young men devised a new method of grinding and polishing lenses to eliminate defects in an image caused by the break-up of white light into colors, and defects resulting from an improper curvature of the lens.

Christian's first astronomical discovery was that of the Nebula of Orion. He later discovered the rings of Saturn, and also one of Saturn's moons, Titan. His love for astronomy, and the need for a precise measure of time in the study of the heavens, turned Christian's attention to the invention of a very accurate pendulum clock.

Louis XIV invited him to France, gave him a comfortable pension, and laid open for him the special delights of hobnobbing with the elite. Christian, however, had no taste for what he saw. Pomp and fashion and rank made him shudder inwardly. He was particularly appalled by the assassination of precious time.

He did fall in love, and he wrote verses to the alluring and famous—or infamous—Ninon de Lenclos, a special friend of many high-placed men.

Science, however, beckoned, and Christian once again devoted all his energies to the unraveling of Nature's secrets.

Delicate of health, he went back to his homeland twice to seek a change of climate, but he returned finally to remain in France to work on physics in general, in optics, and astronomy. Meanwhile, he spent some time on original inventions, improved various scientific devices, and constructed large telescopes.

The magnification of a telescope, as we noted in our discussion of Galileo, depends upon the ratio of the focal length of the objective to the focal length of the eyepiece. Christian used objective lenses of very long focal length. In fact, the focal lengths were so great that Christian mounted his lenses on poles placed far apart. These assemblies became known as "aerial telescopes."

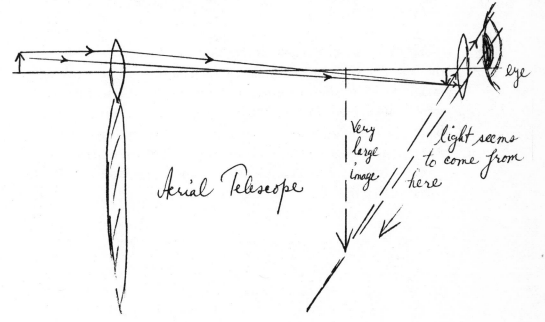

Christian also invented in miniature a sort of mechanical sky, or "planetary machine," which could show the motions of the planets—the forerunner of the present-day planetarium.

In physics, we still use a very fine eyepiece that Christian invented. It is an almost perfect device that overcomes a common defect, color spread. We also use constantly the "Huygens Principle" in the study of light:

When light spreads out, each point on the wave front acts as a new source of light, sending out waves of its own. The new wave front is then the envelope of these new little ones. . . .

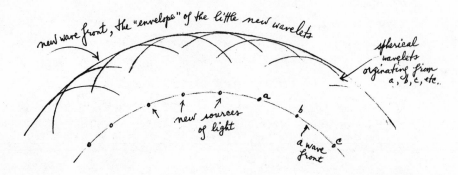

Christian, of course, wrote books about his studies, among the best known being *Treatise on Light* and *Cosmotheros,* an imaginative creation, dealing, as he said, with "The celestial worlds discovered, or conjectures concerning the inhabitants, plants, and productions of the worlds in the planets."

So Christian, you see, took us directly out into space and spoke of other-world beings. Here is his conception of Martians—delightful, furry, flitting beings:

Christian Huygens made some notable discoveries about Mars. He was the first to detect the great triangular expanse on Mars called "Syrtis Major," which is likely to be an area of vegetation—perhaps grassy plains where Christian's Martians romp and flit with nary a care.

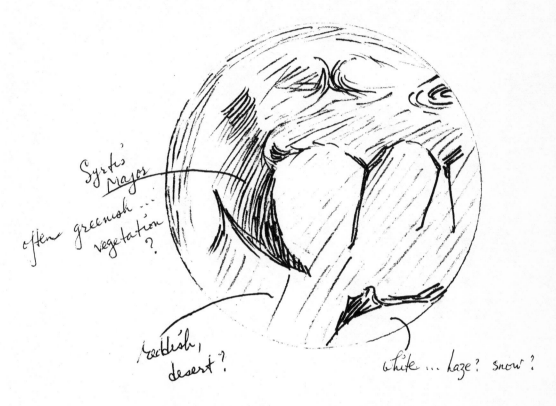

Syrtis Major
often greenish...
vegetation?

reddish,
desert?

white ... haze? snow?

Earthly cares, however, took their toll with Christian. After years of tremendous scientific endeavors, despite his frail constitution, and after a life of careful attention to his enormous correspondence in the interests of science and humanity, Christian Huygens died on June 8, 1695, at the age of 66.

"Any mans death diminishes me, because I am involved in Mankinde. And therefore never send to know for whom the bell tolls; it tolls for thee."

Newton

9

Isaac Newton

1642-1727

The poet Alexander Pope once wrote:

> Nature and Nature's laws lay hid in night:
> God said, let Newton be! and all was light.

Isaac Newton was born at Woolsthorpe, England, on Christmas Day in 1642, the same year in which the exhausted and abused Galileo died. Little Isaac never did see his father, who died before the boy was born. Three years later, Isaac's mother remarried, and it was then decided that Isaac would live with one of his grandmothers.

In school, little Isaac seemed not very bright. Perhaps it was that he felt abandoned by his mother, and even by his grandmother, for, at the age of twelve, his mother and grandmother sent him away to school, in the town of Grantham. There, he lived in the house of a stranger, an apothecary.

Isaac's studies improved. Perhaps a single event brought about a change in attitude. A bully in the school delighted in teasing the smaller boys and in pushing them around. One day this browbeater attacked Isaac, pummeling him and kicking him in the shins. To the astonishment of all the onlookers, Isaac flew at his assailant with both fists flying. Astounded and reeling from the unexpected counterattack, the terrified bully surrendered, gasping and tottering.

From that day on Isaac became outstanding in his classes. Furthermore, he was a leader in the activities outside the classroom. He began making splendid little windmills that actually worked, and kites that flew. Newton also made clocks that ran by water power, and sun dials and a carriage which a person could propel by using his arms or legs to activate moving parts inside.

(Leonardo, you remember, had designed a boat which operated reasonably well by the application of man.)

In 1656, when Isaac was fourteen, his mother returned to him. Her second husband had died. She soon took Isaac out of school and set him to farming. But his heart wasn't in it. Agriculture was for others, but not for Newton. He yearned to return to his studies. He now craved as much education as it was possible to secure, and we are indebted to his shrewd uncle, who first sent him back to his classes and then on to Trinity College, Cambridge, where he worked for his board and room.

Young Newton studied the work of Kepler and of the mathematicians of the time. He kept a notebook to jot down his ideas. Such a habit is a useful one to develop, for often some casual idea jotted down by a youth turns out to be extremely important in later years. Newton wrote out some mathematical ideas that much later led to his invention of the differential calculus. He also studied halos around the moon, and tracked a comet.

In the year 1665, a terrible scourge—the Great Plague— spread from London to Cambridge. Authorities closed the college down so that students would not infect one another.

Newton left the college reluctantly. But, facing up to the situation, he returned to his farm home. Here, studying even harder, he thought up the conception of centrifugal force and its application to the motion of planets. A question constantly nagged him: What is it that makes the planets go around the sun?

True, Kepler had found *how* the planets moved. But he had not discovered *why* they moved as they did. Was there a cause? There must be. What was it? He also began to experiment with lenses, prisms, and chemicals.

His work with prisms eventually led him to one of the greatest discoveries of all time—that *ordinary white light is made up of all the colors we know.* Others had believed that the *prism* put the color into the white light.

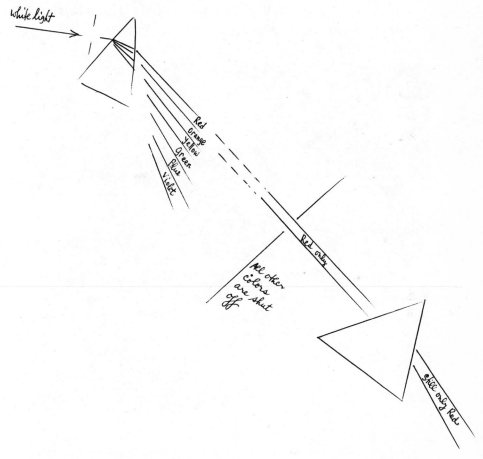

Here is what Newton did: He allowed a narrow beam of light to fall upon a prism. He obtained the spectrum, which others had seen. Now, however, he took one section of this spectrum, the red, and let it pass through a second prism. If the prism puts color in, he reasoned, it follows that this red light should come out with a full colorful spectrum donated by the second prism. The red light, however, came out simply red. The prism had added nothing. The same effect occurred with all the other separate colors.

Other early thoughts of Newton led also to great discoveries. He had been thinking about gravity, and about falling objects, and one day, as he was musing in the garden, he observed an apple fall from a great apple tree. There was the apple, securely on the branch. Then it fell.

Why did it fall? wondered Newton. Earth pulled it. How far does the pulling effect of earth extend? Can it be pulling upon the moon? If so, why doesn't the moon fall toward earth? It does. It does! thought Newton. It does fall toward earth. But, at the same time, it flies off to the side, and it is this side speed which it acquired when it was first propelled somehow past the earth that *keeps it from falling all the way down to earth.*

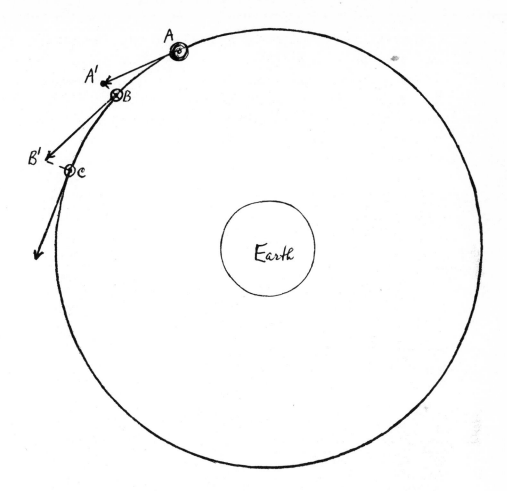

That is, through some event, the moon was propelled past the earth. Thus, the side speed starts to take it from A to A_1. But the earth pulls it so that it arrives at B. Actually, it falls all the time from A to B, but the total fall amounts to A_1B. The moon would be at A_1 in, say, one second if there were no earth near-by, or if earth did not affect it.

The moon retains its side speed at all times as it courses around the earth. From B, its side speed would logically take it to B_1. But, again, earth's pull makes it arrive at C instead of B_1. In this way, the moon keeps revolving around the earth. It is kept from flying away from the earth by being forced to *fall* all the time.

To verify his inspired conception that gravity is universal, and stretches through space, but is weaker at greater distances, Newton worked out some mathematics. He already had the idea that if an object is twice as far away from the center of the earth, the gravitational pull on it would be one fourth; if the object is three times as far away, the pull would be one ninth. The pull is inversely proportional to the square of the distance.

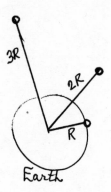

In the diagram, *above,* let us take R as about 4,000 miles. At a distance of 2R, an object feels a pull of one fourth of what its weight is at the surface of the earth. At 3R, the pull is one ninth the pull at the surface.

The moon, on the average, is about 240,000 miles from the earth. Thus, it is $\dfrac{240,000}{4,000}$, or 60 times, farther from the center of the earth than is an object on the earth's surface. The earth's gravitational pull, then, would be $\left(\dfrac{1}{60}\right)^2$, or $\dfrac{1}{3600}$ th of what it is at earth's surface.

"If I use the known radius of the earth," Newton speculated, "will the moon fall, or gravitate, the right amount? After all, we *know* how much it does fall—is this the amount that I can calculate from my assumed law?"

102

The missing piece to the puzzle concerned the earth's radius. The earth's radius at that time was thought to be 3,436 miles, and Newton was about to use this incorrect figure.

If h_2 is the distance the moon falls in 1 second, and h_1 is the distance an object falls near earth's surface in 1 second, $\dfrac{h_2}{h_1}$ should be equal to $\dfrac{1}{3600}$.

Near the earth's surface, however, an object falls 16 feet in 1 second. That is, h_1 is 16 feet. Accordingly, the moon should fall about h_2, or $\dfrac{16}{3600}$ feet.

Does it? It does. Remember, however, that we are using a much more accurate value for the earth's radius than was established when Newton first worked out his formula. When Newton put in the wrong value, unfortunate fellow, the answer of course failed to check with the expected value.

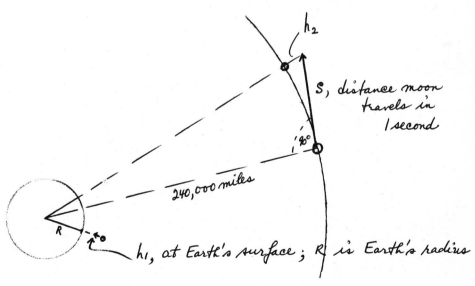

We can calculate h_2 from the above information:

$$(240,000 + h_2)^2 = 240,000^2 + S^2$$
$$(\text{hypotenuse})^2 = (\text{a side})^2 + (\text{other side})^2$$

This gives

$$240,000^2 + 2h_2 \times 240,000 + h_2{}^2 = 240,000^2 + S^2$$

$$\text{or, } h_2 = \frac{S^2}{2 \times 240,000}$$

if we neglect $h_2{}^2$, which is small compared with $2h_2$ $\times$ 240,000.

How much is S? How much does the moon travel in one second? This much was easy to calculate, for the moon travels in approximately a circular path of radius 240,000 miles, and goes around the earth in 27 days, 13 hours, and about 18 minutes. Accordingly, by dividing $2\pi \times 240,000 \times 5280$ by this time (all in *seconds*), we get the moon's advance in 1 second (approximately S).

We have here, then, to compare

$$A) \qquad h_2 = \frac{16}{3600} \text{ feet}$$

with

$$B) \qquad h_2 = \frac{S^2}{2 \times 240,000 \times 5280}$$

where S is in feet.

The two values of h_2, if the same, would prove his law of gravitation.

Of course, the two h_2 values were not close enough to show the assumed law to be right. Newton was baffled and let down in spirits. Remember why: the value he used for earth's radius was not right.

Many years later Newton heard of an investigation which gave a new value for the radius of the earth. In a lightning, breathless calculation he employed the new value of R. He screamed with joy as the right answer leaped out! The moon falls toward the earth! Earth pulls it with a force that follows his law.

He could not rest that night. The greatest physical secret of the universe stood revealed before him—the *Law of*

Universal Gravitation. According to this law, all objects attract each other: the earth and the apple, the sun and the farthest planets, and the stars acting on each other.

The law, in full, states

Any two objects attract each other with a force directly proportional to the mass of one multiplied by the mass of the other, and inversely proportional to the square of the distance between them.

Thus, we say F depends on

$$\frac{M_1 \times M_2}{D^2}$$

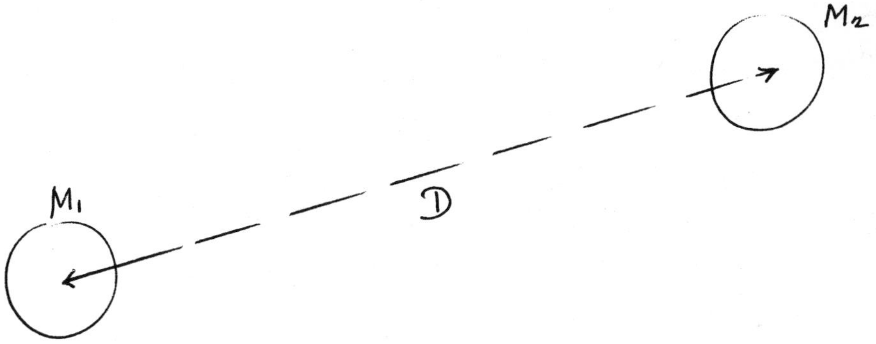

In the above form, the law was sufficient for Newton's thoughts, and its verification justified his insight. If, however, we want to write an *equation*, we might do this

$$F = \frac{GM_1 \times M_2}{D^2}$$

What is G?

If M_1 and M_2 are one unit of mass, and if D is one unit of distance between them, then

$$F = \frac{G \times 1 \times 1}{1^2}, \text{ or } G = F$$

G is the *force* between two unit masses (say 1 gram each), one unit apart (say 1 cm), when they are anywhere in the universe.

And *how much* is G? With what force do these two masses attract each other?

Newton did not know. How do you actually measure G? Is it true that *any* two particles anywhere in the universe really attract each other? And with how much force? Everyone was satisfied that the law, the mathematical form, was right. But with exactly how much force did two masses attract each other?

More than one hundred years passed before we had the answer to that question. An "eccentric" scientist named Henry Cavendish actually performed an experiment which gave him the value of G. Maybe you'd like to look up the "Cavendish experiment."

The value of G is about this much:

.000000000068 of a gram.

That is the value of the pull exerted by one gram mass upon another gram mass when they are 1 cm apart, anywhere in the universe.

Very few people know that Isaac Newton contemplated the possibility in principle of putting an artificial satellite into orbit around the earth. Newton made a sketch showing a projectile being fired horizontally from a mountain top.

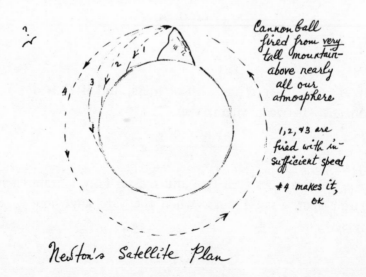

Cannon ball fired from very tall mountain—above nearly all our atmosphere

1, 2, #3 are fired with insufficient speed

#4 makes it, ok

Newton's Satellite Plan

Today, we do this regularly, using his laws of motion and his law of gravitation.

Newton, meanwhile, made some notable advancements in his optical work. In 1668, he built a "reflecting" telescope. He had decided that an objective lens inevitably produces a defect in the image by breaking up the light and introducing a color spread, even though very slight. Accordingly, he used a mirror instead of a lens.

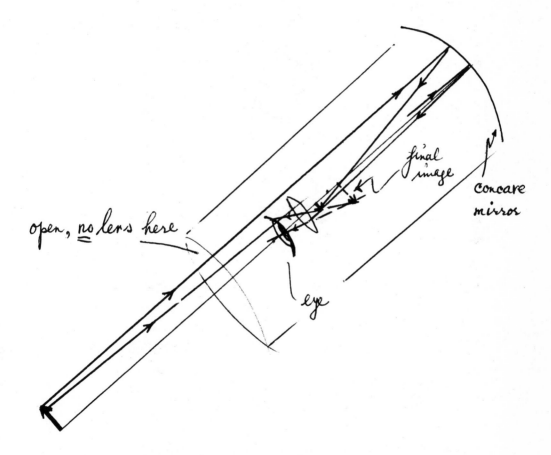

His plans for a telescope, as shown, *above,* seem to force the viewer to put his eye inside the tube. How would you get the image out, so that you could have your eye conveniently outside?

Here is a photograph of Newton's original reflecting telescope, and, remember, the great reflectors of today, such as those at Mount Palomar, are based on Newton's principles.

BROWN BROTHERS

Newton had gone back to the University, in 1667, and his work thereafter was prodigious and original, almost more than should be for one man.

His life, however, was not always in his dreamland of science. He was plagued by controversy. The very capable scientist Robert Hooke (1635-1703) frequently claimed that he had made prior discoveries of certain accomplishments announced by Newton. Hooke made these claims for the law of gravitation and for discoveries in mechanics and optics.

Newton was in despair on such occasions. He often wished that he might work in complete seclusion. Simply to avoid dispute, he would have been satisfied with neither announcing nor publishing the details of his discoveries.

Hooke was outstanding—a genius, possibly. He was, however, by no means, a Newton. The great misfortune of Robert Hooke's life is that he was born to live concurrently with Isaac Newton. In any other epoch, he would have been dominant, as dominant as the sun.

However, with Newton ascendant in the academic heavens, Robert Hooke was like the mere planet Jupiter. Jupiter is a giant planet and even has twelve moons. It is, however, no sun. And Jupiter, with its court of twelve moons, travels around the sun.

The claims of the German mathematician Leibnitz also plagued Newton. Newton had invented the calculus, one of the most beautiful and powerful of all mathematical systems. So, also, had Leibnitz. And Leibnitz's friends vigorously championed their man.

Newton often at this time lost his temper, ridiculing Leibnitz and others who troubled him. Today the scientific world is inclined to believe that the two men both invented the calculus at about the same time, each unaware of the work of the other.

Possibly, in the course of time, it is of no consequence *who* made what discovery. Does Newton care now? Does Leibnitz? Does Hooke? Do we care? Probably we are only glad that they all lived. All sought to find beauty and order in the universe, and to learn the secrets of nature.

We can see that Isaac Newton was reluctant to announce his findings, thus risking controversy, by the following illuminating incident:

The scientist Edmund Halley came to see Newton one day in 1684 to seek the answer to one all-important question.

"What curve," Halley wanted to know, "will a body in space follow if it is orbiting around a much more massive body that exerts a force upon it which varies inversely with the square of the distance?"

"An ellipse," Newton replied, "with the center of force as one focus."

Halley was amazed.

"How do you know?" he asked, nonplussed. "And so quickly!"

Newton shook his head. "It's not quickly," he replied. "I've been working on this type of problem for a long, long time."

Thereupon, Newton opened a large drawer. He pulled out a great mass of papers covered with calculations. His figures related to motions, comets, curves in space, and the action of the moon in causing tides.

Halley stared at this mountain of discoveries and calculations. Newton presented a great bundle of these theoretical calculations to the astounded Halley for his study.

"Why don't you publish all this?" Halley wanted to know.

Newton grimaced. "I have already blamed my own imprudence in the past for parting with so substantial a blessing as my quiet to run after a shadow."

Halley, however, encouraged his friend to bring to light his extraordinary findings, and during the next few years, much of Newton's work was published. Halley himself, at his own expense, brought out a very important part of Newton's vast work in 1687, when the Royal Society, the great scientific body, could not raise the money for the venture.

The world can thank Halley not only for his comet but also for bringing before us more thoroughly a greater luminary than the comet—Isaac Newton.

PHILOSOPHIÆ
NATURALIS
PRINCIPIA
MATHEMATICA.

Autore JS. NEWTON, Trin. Coll. Cantab. Soc. Matheseos Professore Lucasiano, & Societatis Regalis Sodali.

IMPRIMATUR·
S. PEPYS, Reg. Soc. PRÆSES.
Julii 5. 1686.

LONDINI,
Jussu Societatis Regiæ ac Typis Josephi Streater. Prostat apud plures Bibliopolas. Anno MDCLXXXVII.

Title page of one of the greatest scientific books ever written. Can you name 3 other great scientific books?

Newton's great published work, *The Principia,* is a wonder to contemplate even today. It was, of course, a sensation in Newton's time. The brilliant Christian Huygens, the most famous scientist of all at the time of the appearance of *The Principia,* journeyed to England to meet this extraordinary man, Isaac Newton, about whom everyone was talking.

Newton, somehow, found time to concern himself with the fact that King James II was trying to diminish the independent status and freedom of action of the University, and subsequently, he was elected a member of Parliament for Cambridge.

Upon his return to Cambridge from his parliamentary duties in London, Newton suffered a long siege of ill health. Mentally disturbed, he could do nothing worth while for almost two years.

In part, at least, Newton's distress was brought about by the little dog he owned—a dog named "Diamond."

One day, having worked over a great mound of original calculations, Newton walked out into his garden for a breath of air. Upon stepping back indoors, he stood stupefied—the dog had upset a candle, and the entire accumulation of Newton's papers, over which he had labored for years, was on fire.

Many priceless calculations were destroyed.

Newton was inconsolable for a prolonged period of time.

"Diamond, Diamond," Newton whispered. "What have you wrought?"

"It is no wonder," people commented afterward, "that he has almost lost his mind."

When, in the year 1695, Newton regained his health, he left the University. He accepted the position of Warden of the Mint. Later, he became Master of the Mint. He never afterward returned to his heroic labors on anything like his former pace. He scarcely turned out any original scientific work.

Newton's slackened efforts seem to be a common experience with great scientists. A scientist becomes famous for his discoveries, then is offered a high position. He becomes a dean, a president of a college, or the president of a large corporation, at a magnificent salary. And lo! the world loses a brilliant scholar. It gains merely another executive or administrator.

Newton remained in his new post for the rest of his life—thirty years. He did, however, concern himself to a certain extent with science, solving difficult problems which brought international prizes. Despite this activity, he was but a mere shadow of the former Newton.

He served as President of the Royal Society for twenty-four years, from 1703 to 1727, and, of course, he received many honors from all over the world.

Toward the end of his life Newton became intensely interested in theological studies. The older he grew, the more humble he became, once remarking, "I do not know what I may appear to the world, but to myself I seem to have been only like a boy playing on the seashore, and diverting myself in now and then finding a smoother pebble or a prettier shell than ordinary, whilst, the great ocean of truth lay all undiscovered before me."

Among these smoother pebbles were the following:

1. His *laws of motion,* an expansion of Galileo's work:

a) The *first law of motion*: An object at rest remains at rest, unless some force intervenes. An object moving in a straight line with constant speed will maintain the direction and the speed unless some force intervenes.

b) The *second law of motion*: When a force acts upon an object, it accelerates, in the direction of the force, and the amount of the acceleration can be calculated from

$$a = \frac{F}{m}$$

where F is the force acting upon the body of mass m.

c) The *third law of motion*: Action and reaction are equal and opposite. This is the principle upon which rocket propulsion is based; the interior upper wall of the combustion chamber presses the hot gases outward, and they press back upon the interior upper wall, thus communicating thrust.

2. The *Law of Universal Gravitation*, which explains in a precise mathematical way all of Kepler's Planetary Laws— the *ellipse*, with the sun at one focus; the *law of areas;* the *harmonic law*, giving the relation between the period of a planet and its distance from the sun; the motions of falling apples, falling moons, and swishing meteors.

3. The tides on earth, understood through the use of the *Law of Gravitation*.

4. The flaming gaseous tides on the sun, caused by the tugging of the planets.

5. The precession of earth's axis, calculated out to be 26,000 years for a complete turn.

6. The flattening of earth due to spin—diameter is 28 miles shorter from pole to pole than along the axis at right angles to this line.

7. Calculation of the mass of the moon, from the size of spring and neap tides.

8. A homogeneous sphere (such as a uniform planet) acts, in exerting gravitational attraction, as though all its mass were concentrated at a point at its center.

9. A hollow shell acts the same way, as though its mass were all at its center. At interior points, however, the shell exerts no effect.

no force anywhere inside

10. The length of a day of Jupiter can be calculated from the amount of its flattening caused by spin.

11. The weight of a body at the pole is greater than its weight at the equator, because of the lesser distance from the pole to the center of the earth. Example: 195 pounds at the pole is 194 pounds at the equator.

12. Comets are members of the solar system, and travel in ellipses. (Exceptions could occur for comets coming from outside our solar system.)

13. One can calculate how much a planet may be disturbed or may have its orbit perturbed by other planets.

14. The force controlling the moon's flight follows the same law as that acting on bodies launched near the earth.

15. The sun's mass can be calculated if one knows the distance of any planet from the sun and the length of its year.

16. The mass of any planet can be calculated if the planet has an observable moon.

17. White light consists of all colors.

18. He invented the calculus.

These were the principal smoother pebbles of the seashore found by Newton. Yet, he made mistakes. He thought light to be made up of *particles*. He spoke of "absolute time," flowing forward of itself forever at a uniform rate, and "otherwise known as duration;" and he spoke of "absolute space"—a region that really stood still, though all else might move.

Other scientists would correct these mistakes. Yet, they could not have progressed so far into the age of space if that "boy" Newton had not strolled at the seashore.

"If I have seen further than others," Newton once said, *"it is only because I have stood on the shoulders of giants who have come before me."*

For their part, scientists after him could not have seen further, if they had not stood on the shoulders of the giant among giants who came before them. This boy, this giant, died on March 20, 1727. He will never be forgotten.

Herschel

10

William and Caroline Herschel

1738-1822, 1750-1848

A problem in space travel that is bound to come up before long is this: *Where do we go?* I mean after the landings on the moon have become routine, and we've made really good explorations on Mars, Venus, and the rest of our planets, where do we go from there?

Do we go toward any star, at random, hoping that it will turn out to have good—that is, habitable—planets with intelligent beings? Or do we set out toward the *nearest* star?

In the first place, it would seem like sheer space madness to set out on a thousand-year journey toward any star at all, in the hope that it might turn out to have Good Earths of its own, with friendly natives. What if it has no planets with inhabitants? What if it has no planets at all? Do we only mutter, "That's show biz!" then go on to another star for another five hundred or one thousand years?

No, we'll not be going in any such irresponsible and unplanned manner. Before we set out on an interstellar trip—from a planet of our star to a planet of another star—we will wait for some *communication*. We will wait for some message from intelligent beings living on a Good Earth of some star.

What kind of message will we await? We don't know exactly, but it will have to be some radio communication which clearly shows that there is "someone out there." A Morse code type of communication would be okay, of course, or a modulated carrier wave with music on it, or interrupted bursts of energy in a planned pattern—any form that would distinguish the message from electrical space static.

117

Very well, then, we'll wait for communication from a Good Earth of some sun. But don't we have to point our antennas in the direction of such a possible solar system? Of course. And at which star do we point?

This question takes us to the crux of our problem: Not all stars are capable of having planets with life. Some stars are like our sun. They have endured long enough—at least four or five billion years—to have allowed life to reach a level as "advanced" as our earth life. But some stars are young—too young to have planets with advanced life. Others are easily old enough, but they are so small and cool that the zone of adequate warmth around them is narrow, with planets likely to be outside. Other stars are exploding. Still others are thinking about exploding.

William Herschel knew all this. In fact, he once wrote that the heavens are like a garden, where plants are growing in all possible stages—some barely now shooting, some already in leaf, some flowering, some bearing seed, some decaying. The heavens, Herschel believed, contain all kinds of worlds—some old, some dead, some young and thriving, some at this moment coming into existence.

William Herschel also knew that some stars, or suns, are red, others blue, yellow, green, or purple. He gazed at the heavens throughout his long life, feeling as though he belonged out there.

Frederick William Herschel (he liked to be known as William) was born in Hannover, Germany. He was raised as a musician, because his father was a competent musician, an oboe player. The father wanted his many children to have "kultur." The mother, however, was a strong-headed, nononsense type of woman of considerable ignorance, who firmly believed that such occupations as reading and writing and books and music would only get a person into trouble.

"I can't read," she used to say, standing up straight and strong. "And you see I have been successful in life."

Herschel's mother permitted the two girls to learn only household management, sewing, and cooking. She took pride in instructing them in these skills, rather efficiently.

William, the fourth child, longed to leave home. At the age of seventeen, he became oboist to the Hannoverian Guards, and made with them an extended trip to England. He stayed with the guards for two years, then detached himself from the regiment and decided to remain in England, where he began work as a musician—composer, organist, and instructor.

Some years later Herschel made a short trip back home. His sister, Caroline, then told her brother that she too hoped to escape the confines of the home. William, however, returned to England alone. Then, seven years after the death of their father, he visited in Germany again, and this time he returned to England with Caroline. The world of astronomy profited immeasurably from this move.

William had been reading some books on science and mathematics. The volumes on astronomy gripped him so that he could scarcely put the books out of his hands. He rented a small telescope, viewed the heavens, entranced, and drew Caroline also into the observations. Then William set about building his own telescope.

At this point, one of their brothers, Alex, came to England. Alex was an expert machinist. You can imagine what happened next. All three of them turned with a breathlessness to making telescopes and to studying the heavens. Caroline, additionally, had to shop, sew, cook, and manage the house, as her mother had taught her.

Astronomy, however, came first, along with the care of her brothers, particularly William, who was becoming utterly fascinated with his celestial garden. Caroline, writing in her journal, told of his enthusiasm:

. . . by way of keeping him alive I was constantly obliged to feed him by putting the victuals by bits into his mouth. This was once the case when, in order to finish a seven-foot mirror, he had not taken his hands from it for sixteen hours together. In general he was never unemployed at meals, but always at those times contriving or making drawings of whatever came in his mind. Generally, I was obliged to read to him whilst he was at the turning lathe, or polishing mirrors—*Don Quixote, Arabian Nights' Entertainments,* the novels of Sterne, Fielding, etc.; serving tea and supper without interrupting the work with which he was engaged. I became, in time, as useful a member of the workshop as a boy might be to his master in the first year of his apprenticeship. . . .

She became much more. She began to observe the heavens regularly, and when William was observing, she took down in a notebook the observations, descriptions, and telescope-position readings, which he dictated. Caroline, as William knew, was an excellent assistant.

William and Caroline regularly stayed up all night when the skies were clear, and of course slept during part of the day, though not for long. They had to be at work on new telescopes.

So passed the years—long, wonderful years full of heavenly discoveries. They discovered double stars, changing stars whose light grew brighter and dimmer and brighter again, luminous regions called "nebulae," many of which we now know are galaxies—other universes in space; and comets and a planet!

William, who knew the heavens to a star, had spotted a new bright object. He followed it night after night, calculating its orbit. The object was about twice the distance of Saturn from the sun. It moved in a near circular path. William knew that it must be a planet. It became known as "Uranus," for the God of the Universe.

This was the first planet discovered by "modern" man. Other planets, Mercury, Venus, Earth, Jupiter, and Saturn, had "always" been known, even in the dimmest antiquity.

William was now world-famous. The King sent for him to bring his telescope to Court for a demonstration. Meanwhile,

Caroline, remaining busy at home, wondered if William was getting proper meals and rest.

Upon William's return home, the King offered money for the building of a telescope and an observatory. Delighted, William and Caroline pressed local craftsmen into service.

When this huge telescope was finished, William discovered the sixth and seventh moons of Saturn. (We now know of nine.) He also discovered two moons of Uranus. (We now know of five.)

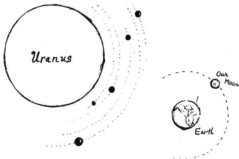

Uranus and its moons, compared to Earth and Moon

At about this time there came a change in the circumstances of this household. In the year 1783, William Herschel married. The new wife and the sister, Caroline, did not take to each other.

Accordingly, the married couple went to live in a large house at Slough, while Caroline found some rooms to rent. Still, she went nightly to William's place to assist him in his observations of the heavens. Caroline often used her own smaller telescope for observations, and she herself discovered many nebulae—Island Universes—and eight comets.

In their study and close observation, this brother and sister team had been slowly across the entire visible heavens, deliberately four times, each sweep taking about two years. William catalogued 2,500 nebulae; he discovered more than 800 double stars, which, he showed, revolved around each other; he made estimates of the brightness of hundreds of stars; and he measured star motions.

Besides making all these discoveries and observations, William built with his own hands more than four hundred parabolic mirrors for Newtonian type telescopes.

William, by close study of the stars, was able to make an astounding discovery—that our sun was on its way through the heavens toward the constellation Hercules, with the earth and the other planets accompanying it.

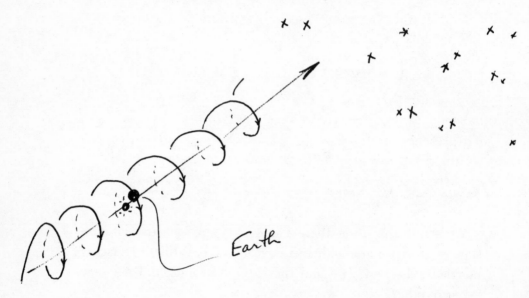

Earth

Today, we know that the sun's speed relative to the star Vega, in the constellation Lyra, is about 12 miles per second.

William found that in one part of the sky the stars generally seemed to be separating from each other, while in the opposite side of the sky, the stars seemed to be in general drawing closer to each other. At right angles, in both directions, the stars seemed to be keeping their unchanging positions. This is like the situation we experience when we drive down an avenue lined on both sides by trees. The trees toward which we drive seem to open out, while those behind us close in.

William tried also to estimate the size and shape of the Milky Way. There was nothing in the heavens that lacked for his attention, but the individual stars, each with its own personality, were his especial favorites. He wondered a great deal about these distant possible solar systems.

Today, after profiting from the work of the Herschels, we can say something more about these world systems. Stars which are huge and hot will have a short life of only some millions of years. Though they have wide zones of good, or habitable, warmth where possible planets might circulate, they will explode and sizzle their planets long before any advanced life could begin to stroll on those surfaces. As we have indicated previously, the very small cool stars, on the other hand, though they last trillions of years, have zones of habitable warmth that are extremely narrow. Any circulating planets simply may not have the good fortune of settling within the boundaries of these suitable zones. Hence, life is unlikely near these cool stars, surrounded by frozen regions, as they are almost entirely.

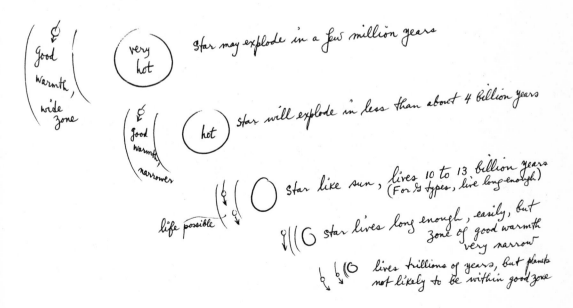

123

And what exactly happens in general to a star that begins to lose its stability? The star heats up, expands enormously, and then cools because of expansion. After this point of development has been reached, the star may begin to swell and contract alternately. On the other hand, the star may go on to contract rapidly and cause such heating up that violent nuclear reactions take place, and it *explodes*, blowing itself to smithereens. Only a small part of this star remains, a cool "White Dwarf" that fades from view and goes into oblivion.

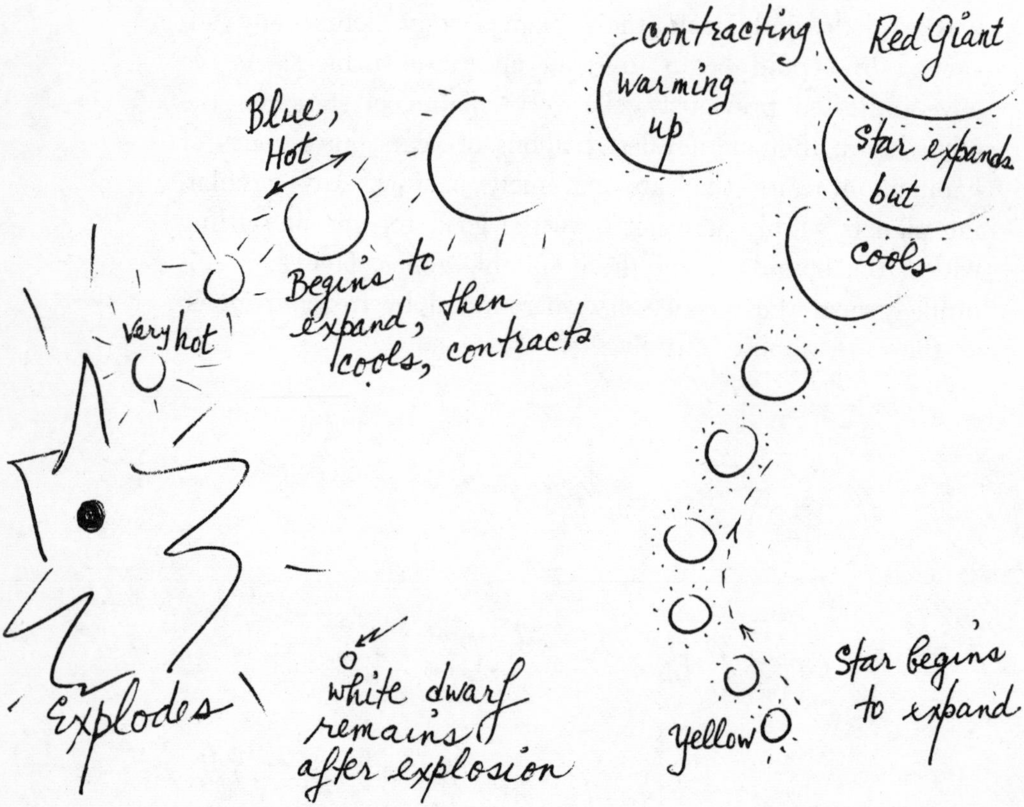

Blue, Hot

contracting warming up

Red Giant

star expands but cools

Very hot

Begins to expand, then cools, contracts

Star begins to expand

yellow

Explodes

white dwarf remains after explosion

Will our sun behave in this way? It is expected that the sun will go through this routine in about eight billion years. As you can see, we have plenty of time in which to pack our suitcases and prepare to leave for the planet of another star.

And now, where will we go after we have explored all of our planets?

We'll wait for messages from *F* and *G* stars. No use bothering about the others. To avoid receiving a great deal of space static, we'll study those *F* and *G* stars which are off the plane of the Milky Way, because noise from space in our Milky Way plane—or our galactic plane—is forty times as great as from the expanse of space in other directions.

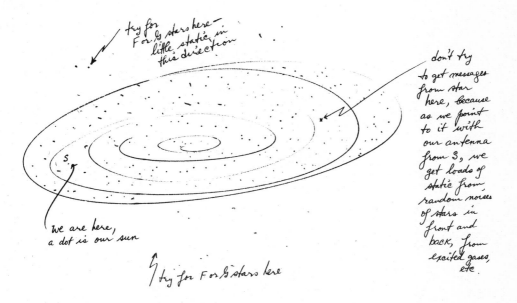

try for
F or G stars here—
little static in
this direction

don't try
to get messages
from star
here, because
as we point
to it with
our antenna
from S, we
get loads of
static from
random noises
of stars in
front and
back, from
excited gases,
etc.

we are here,
a dot is our sun

try for F or G stars here

Then, after receiving a message, an invitation to visit, we may set off. Would you like to go?

William Herschel and Caroline put us among the stars, and we've never been the same since. William lived to be 84 years—the time it takes for the planet Uranus to orbit the sun once. Caroline lived to the age of 98.

William had one son, John Herschel. John, like others, stood on the shoulders of the giants before him, and he became a great astronomer himself. Yet, among the giants named Herschel, my favorite, somehow, is Caroline.

Lobatchevsky

Nikolai Ivanovitch Lobatchevsky

1793-1856

Often I receive letters in which I am asked, "How does one measure the distance to a star?"

Moreover, many people are skeptical about the distances that are mentioned by scientists in speaking of astronomical bodies. They seem to imply, "You didn't measure the distance with a tape, so how come you think you know it?"

We don't have to go out there with a tape measure. In fact, we don't have to go out there at all. What's the matter with this method:

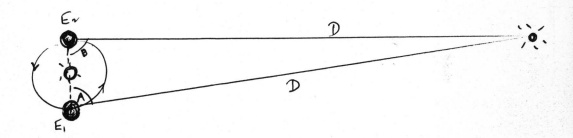

When earth, in its annual revolution around the sun, is at E_1 we sight the star whose distance D we want to know, and we measure the angle A. Six months later, we sight the star again, and measure the angle B. We know the distance E_1 to E_2: $2 \times 93,000,000$, or $186,000,000$ miles.

(One way of getting the distance to the sun is simply by sending a radar pulse to the sun and have it bounce back, timing the round trip. We of course take half of this total time, in seconds, and multiply it by $186,000$, which is the speed of the radar waves in miles per second.)

Here now we have a triangle with one side known, and we have two angles. We draw this triangle to scale, with, say, 186,000,000 miles (for the side) as 1.86 inches. We draw the two angles with a protractor.

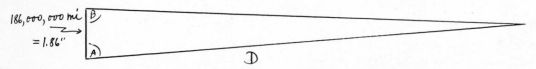

We then simply measure D, using our scale of 1.86 inches for 186,000,000 miles. (Or, we solve the problem by trigonometry.)

Those who write me often want further information.

"How far are the farthest stars? Does it all go on and on—forever? To infinity? I can't conceive of endless space, going on and on . . ."

Others write to relate such impressions as the following: "I've read that the universe has a definite size. It does *not* go on and on. But I can't visualize what this means . . ."

Such has been the experience of people for thousands of years. They can't visualize an infinite universe, and they can't visualize a finite universe.

I, too, have been puzzled by such considerations. At least, I can now visualize the meaning of a *finite* universe, and, incidentally, one that is at the same time unbounded. This sounds like eating your cake and having it too, but it really isn't. In such a universe we would set out in a straight line and go and go and go, and eventually *come back* from the other side.

To explain this situation, let us start first with a billiard ball on which there lives a flat bug. By flat, we mean that he is *really* flat: he has length and width, but *no thickness*. This bug can't lift his head into space, the direction away from the billiard ball surface.

One day he says, "I wonder how big the universe is. I think I'll take a trip and see if I can find out."

So he sets out. He travels in a "straight" line, and keeps going farther and farther. Lo and behold! One day he *returns* home.

Naturally, he is amazed and unbelieving for a while.

"How can it be? I went in a straight line! How could I get back?"

Of course, you and I know what his trouble is. He is two-dimensional, and to him, with his nose along the surface, the path that he followed was a straight line. There couldn't be a line any straighter. Isn't a straight line the shortest distance between two points? Wasn't he traveling along the shortest distance?

You and I, however, enjoying our third dimension of "upness," or height, can see that what he considers to be a straight line is, *to us,* a curve. He is of two dimensions—length and width; and we are of three dimensions—length, width, and height.

Therefore, if we set out traveling through space in what to us is a straight line, we might well return. A *four-dimensional* being, however,—we'll consider the fourth dimension later—would realize what the situation is. He would simply murmur, "What *they* take to be a straight line, is, to me, a curve. Of course, they must come back. Where else could they go?"

You and I might realize what the trouble is, but there is nothing we can do about it. It is the same with the bug. He might well realize what the "true" situation is, but there is nothing that he can do about it.

What *can* he do? Can he wander aimlessly over his spherical surface trying to avoid the straight line which fools him? So what? Has he found a straighter line along which to travel in order to measure the length of his universe? No other line is shorter or straighter than the one he first chose. They are all *longer,* if he wants to travel "all the way".

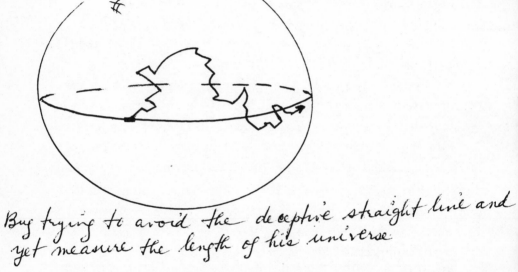

But trying to avoid the deceptive straight line and yet measure the length of his universe

So it is likewise with us. What can we do to avoid the deceptive straight line as determined by our surveying instruments, our telescopes, and our rays of light? What can we do to travel along a *really* straight line? Nothing. There is nothing we can do.

The straight line is inevitable. Every other pathway would result in a longer journey, so we already had selected our "straight line". Therefore, we could speak of living in a finite universe that has no boundaries.

The great Greek geometer Euclid believed that space is flat. By this he meant that a straight line is a straight line and no monkey business. In that case, if one sets out in a

Euclidean straight line he will *not* come back, but will keep on going forever, or else he may reach some sort of fence.

This is the point we considered previously—that for several thousand years people have been unable to visualize either an infinite universe or one that ends. The philosopher Immanuel Kant used to say that Euclid is obviously right; straight is straight, the universe is flat, space is Euclidean and one can sense all this by intuition.

Incidentally, according to Euclid, the three angles of any triangle add up to 180°. It goes like this

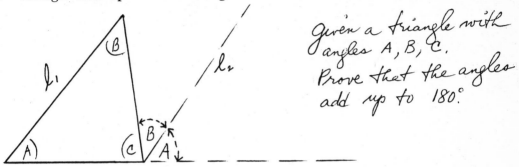

The proof can be given in this manner. Draw line L_2 parallel to L_1. Then put in the angles A and B over again, as shown. Now, it is staring us in the face: $C + B + A = 180°$.

In building up his geometry, which even now high school students study, Euclid used the following statement: Through a point P outside of a straight line L, one and only one straight line can be drawn parallel to L.

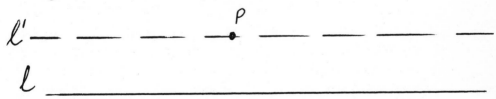

Only one line L', Euclid said, can be drawn parallel to L, and never meet it, no matter how far L' and L are extended.

Euclid couldn't prove this statement. He frankly used it as an assumption, saying, "I'll accept it, and go on from there."

This statement is known as Euclid's Fifth Postulate (or his Axiom XI), and for nearly two thousand years men accepted it all over Planet Earth, until a Russian named Nikolai Ivanovitch Lobatchevsky began to give the matter some serious thought in the nineteenth century.

Nikolai, the second of three sons of a minor government official, was born in the province of Nijni Novgorod, famous for its colorful fairs.

The father died when Kolya (Russian diminutive for Nikolai) was seven years old. The mother then took her boys to live in Kazan, where she could get them into the school system as free scholars.

From the beginning, Kolya was outstanding in the classics and mathematics. By the age of fourteen, he was ready for the University. Fortunately, there in the very city was Kazan University having recently been founded. Kolya began his university studies in 1807, and his exceptional abilities quickly became apparent.

By the age of eighteen he had his master's degree, and by twenty he was appointed Assistant Professor. Three years later he became full Professor. He taught mathematics, physics, and astronomy.

Lobatchevsky did his work so well and so easily that the officials appointed him also University Librarian and Curator of the University Museum. Furthermore, he was appointed a kind of "overseer" or "supervisor" over the political opinions of students from the entire Kazan area. The students he was to oversee ranged from the elementary graduates through the postgraduate level.

This, clearly, was an unfortunate assignment for a scholar, or for anyone else. Many people lost respect for Lobatchevsky because of this Big Brother aspect of his duties. He struggled to steer a middle course between pleasing the government, which expected him to keep students in line, and pleasing the students, who expected freedom.

Lobatchevsky was promoted to the position of Dean of the Department of Mathematics and Physics. In 1827, he became the Rector, or President of the University. He took all his work seriously, preferring to pitch in and to do things himself whenever possible, rather than to "delegate authority".

Lobatchevsky kept up his lively interest in the University library and museum, often working industriously among the books and curios, in his shirtsleeves. On one such occasion, a visitor, believing Lobatchevsky to be the janitor, asked the scientist where he could find a certain museum piece. Lobatchevsky immediately assumed command of the situation.

He conducted the visitor to the spot and proceeded to give an explanation about the object. From there he led the guest on a tour, lecturing for two hours on all phases of everything they saw. The visitor was astounded at the intelligence and charm of this "janitor," and finally pulled out his purse and started to offer a tip. Lobatchevsky growled at him and walked away.

That evening there was a reception at the residence of the Governor. At the banquet table, in formal attire, Lobatchevsky and the visitor met face to face. The man had difficulty eating his meal. Lobatchevsky laughed and ate very well.

The amazing point about Lobatchevsky's life is this: While they were saddling him and loading him down with duties, he was carrying on a far larger activity, in secret. He worked at home night after night. Gradually, but relentlessly, Nikolai Lobatchevsky was dethroning the great geometer Euclid.

His mathematical work first came to light in 1826, when Lobatchevsky presented a report before the Physical-Mathematical Society of Kazan. Most of the scholars, however, failed to recognize its importance, and his report was just about forgotten.

Moreover, there were vital and startling events, which now and then distracted the Russian scholars at Kazan. In 1830, for example, the cholera plague burst upon Kazan.

Lobatchevsky, pitching right in, and calling upon his scientific mind, ordered a fight against the cholera. Putting an end to much wailing and moaning, he invited all the faculty men, their families, and the students to come and live at the University. There he instituted measures of isolation and strict sanitation. His approach proved successful, and of 660 residents at the University, only 16 died—a remarkable record compared with the wholesale deaths that were occurring in the regions outside the University grounds.

I remember reading of the measures taken in the eighteenth century by Katherine II when smallpox epidemics were breaking out all over Russia. Katherine, who was well informed of the scientific progress made in the fight against smallpox, ordered her friend Gregory Orlov to take charge of the situation with a firm hand. Orlov dispersed crowds where people were infecting each other. He imposed isolation and strict sanitation. Having been vaccinated himself, he walked about unafraid. Orlov succeeded in wiping out the epidemic.

Lobatchevsky was such a man. Of strong will, he acted decisively whenever the situation really demanded it, and when he was at work on his mathematical problems.

Political changes continually occurred. During one such change, Nikolai Ivanovitch Lobatchevsky, Rector of the University, Professor, Scholar, devoted servant for forty years, lost his job. Or jobs. Such was his reward.

He was now fifty-three years old. His health was failing, and his troubles did not improve it. When, as a climax, his son died, Lobatchevsky's health failed almost completely.

In 1855, Kazan University celebrated the fiftieth anniversary of its founding, and the frail Lobatchevsky came to the celebration to present a volume of his lifetime work—a book on the new geometry. He had dictated this volume, for he had not been able to write it himself. He was blind.

Several months later, on February 24, 1856, Kolya Lobatchevsky died.

What was this new geometry? Why is Lobatchevsky rightly called "The Copernicus of Mathematics"?

Lobatchevsky had challenged Euclid's Fifth Postulate, just as Copernicus had challenged the notion that the earth stood still. It is as simple as all that. Yes, but, once a person has challenged a basic axiom or assumption upon which all of astronomy or all of geometry is based, he has changed the world. The new axioms will, inevitably, *mathematically* change everything—all conclusions of importance.

Lobatchevsky said, "I can think of the possibility that more than one straight line can be drawn through the point *P*, and these lines will never intersect the line *L*, even if they are extended forever.

His statement doesn't look reasonable, does it? Well, he said, "I'm thinking of a surface which is not a 'plane' as is this piece of paper. I'm thinking of this sort of a saddle-shaped surface, a hyperbolic surface."

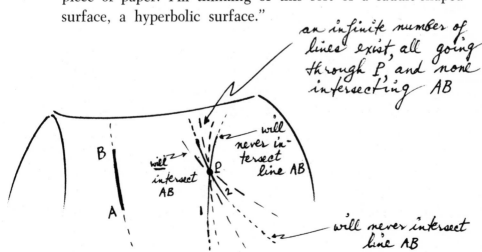

135

Lobatchevsky thus challenged Euclid's assumption that the Fifth Postulate is necessary for a complete and consistent geometry. One can see from the diagram that, if we stay within the limiting lines 1 and 2, we can have as many lines as we want, all of them being "straight" for the surface and none of which will intersect *AB*. Such lines, or curves, are called "geodesics."

On the surface of the earth, we do not have Euclid's geometry. And, furthermore, what reason do we have for believing that the geometry of space is Euclidean? Lobatchevsky wasn't maintaining anything about space, particularly. He was a mathematician, and he contended that he could build another kind of geometry.

This he did. On his surface, by the way, the three angles of a triangle, do *not* add up to 180°. They add up to less.

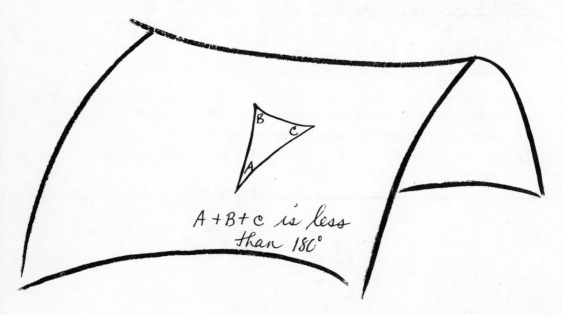

A + B + c is less than 180°

Of course, this is just the start. We can imagine how Euclid's books on geometry would all be altered if we began with a few basic changes and simply continued to consider every imaginable phase of curves, lines, angles, and figures.

At about the same time that Lobatchevsky was working all this out in Russia, there was a young Hungarian named János Bolyai (1802-1860) who was doing the same thing! They didn't know about each other's work.

Bolyai's father was an amateur mathematician, and from him the youthful János received the impulse and encouragement to study mathematics. János progressed so rapidly after he began to wonder about Euclid's Fifth Postulate that on November 3, 1823, when he was only twenty-one years old, he wrote to his father about his non-Euclidean geometry, "From nothing I have created another wholly new world."

János was a rather dashing young man, very athletic, fond of music, and an excellent marksman and duellist. He was so impetuous, brash, able and forward that, when he served in the cavalry, his fellow-officers resented him. They would occasionally gang up on him with ridicule and insult. On one such occasion, János, contemptuous of the lot of them, simply challenged them all to a duel, thirteen of them!

"One at a time," he suggested, "and as I dispose of each, I want a few minutes of rest to play my violin, before trouncing the next one."

The officers, glowering at him with hatred, took him on. János started to defeat them one by one, and between duels, he played his violin. He whipped every one of them.

His mathematical work, as we have said, was along the same lines as Lobatchevsky's, so he, too, is credited with devising *hyperbolic space.*

In consequence of the work of Lobatchevsky and Bolyai, it became quite clear that Euclid's Fifth Postulate—and consequently his entire geometry—definitely had no longer any privileged status. If the parallel postulate were true at all, it would have to be established the hard way, namely by experiment.

The field of geometrical creativity was now wide open. The next formidable stride comes as the result of the German mathematician Bernhard Riemann (1826-1866), who decided to construct a geometry on other sorts of surfaces. "Why just hyperbolic?" Riemann pondered. In particular, Riemann developed in detail the geometry of the spherical surface, among others, in which Euclid's Fifth Postulate does not hold. Thus, on the spherical surface, you cannot draw even one straight line.

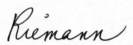

CULVER PICTURES, INC.

(A "geodesic," or great circle is here the equivalent of the straight line since the distance between any two points on a sphere is shortest when you follow a great circle. That is the way a ship sails on the oceans, as you know. It sails along a great circle which passes between the point of departure and the point of destination. Airplanes and rockets, too, are aimed to follow the geodesic below them.)

Here, then, is a sketch of the situation on a sphere:

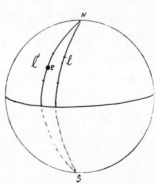

On a sphere, any two geodesics always intersect. In fact, they intersect in two points, so that it is impossible to draw even one line, L', which is parallel to L.

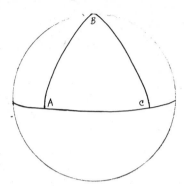

Angles $A + B + C = 270°$, not $180°$. And the angles of other triangles, also, add up to more than $180°$, though less than $270°$.

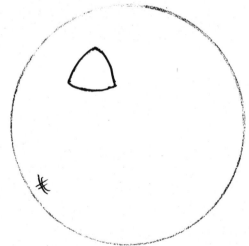

We must not forget to mention also the work of Herman Minkowski, who thought along these lines and began to relate these geometries to the actual universe. Minkowski went so far as to construct a geometry made up of three dimensions of space, and a fourth dimension—time.

"Space by itself," he maintained, "is meaningless. And time by itself is without meaning. They are mere shadows. We live in a universe fused out of space and time—a universe of space-time."

We must, of course, a little later, show what Albert Einstein did with non-Euclidean geometry and space-time.

Meanwhile, here is a summing up of these ideas:

Euclid: Space is flat in any plane we choose; it goes on and on; it is infinite, with no boundaries; parallel lines never meet; the Fifth Postulate holds sway; the three angles of a triangle add up to 180°.

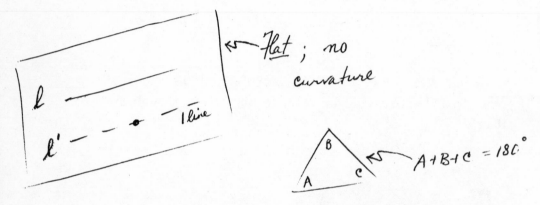

Lobatchevsky and Bolyai: Geometry of nonflatness can be consistent; hyperbolic geometry is constructable and perfectly possible for the real world; Euclid's Fifth Postulate does not hold in hyperbolic geometry, since we can have any number of geodesics *L'* that we want; the three angles of a triangle add up to less than 180°; this geometry may be true for the universe—the answer must come from experiment.

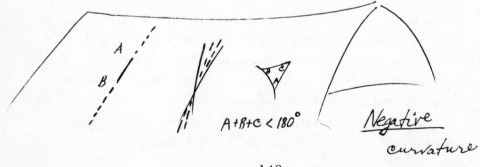

Riemann: Geometry on any type of surface can be constructed; for spherical surface geometry Euclid's Fifth Postulate does not hold, since any two geodesics *intersect*—in fact, in two points; the three angles of a triangle add up to more than 180°; spherical geometry may be true for the universe—the answer must come from experiment.

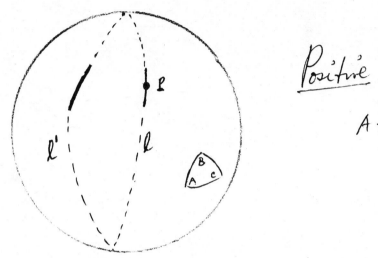

Positive Curvature

$$A + B + C > 180°$$

Minkowski and Einstein began to go out into the real universe, trying to tailor a suitable geometry to all space.

What did Einstein finally achieve? On whose shoulders did he stand to observe the grandest view? Can we really travel straight and straight and straight and come back? It is a possibility.

Faraday

12

Michael Faraday

1791-1867

What is the distinguishing trait of an outstanding scientist that sets him apart from the scientists we commonly meet? I was discussing this point with a friend the other day. The question is a complicated one. We agreed, however, on one feature: the really creative scientist, we believe, is one who allows an unexpected incident to capture his imagination.

The outstanding scientist permits the *unusual* to take hold of him and follows open-mindedly in the direction it points, whereas the routine scientist is annoyed by unexpected circumstances for fear such a turn of events might force a departure from his projected plan of research. He rejects the unexpected, the gift from nature, and labors mightily with his nose to the grindstone and his vision in the dust. He gets something done—something he planned. That's about all.

One day, in 1820, in Denmark, an oustanding scientist, a creative one, was working with an electrical circuit. He closed the switch, and out of the corner of his eye, he noted an unusual occurrence.

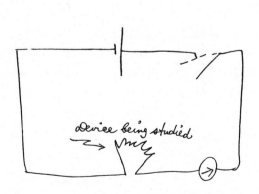

Device being studied

A near-by compass needle moved! This incident had nothing whatever to do with his experiment. The compass needle was there by accident—it didn't belong there at all. But the magnetic needle had moved.

What would a good, dull, hard-working scientist have done? He would have shoved the compass needle away, perhaps putting it on the shelf where it belonged. For him it would have been a distraction and a nuisance.

This man's name was Hans Christian Oersted (1777-1851). I am sure that a number of scientists before Oersted noticed such effects, by accident, and may have been slightly annoyed by this unexpected behaviour of a compass needle. But Oersted was different. He was amazed at what he saw.

A switch is closed in an electrical circuit and a magnetic compass needle near-by responds? Why? Why could this be? He opened the switch, and the magnetic needle moved again. He brought it closer and it moved even more.

Imagine! *Electricity produces magnetism.* Oersted forgot all about his original plan, and went after this unexpected event—electricity produces magnetism!

And what about Isaac Newton and that apple? An ordinary scientist would have said, "I wish those apples would stop falling, I'm thinking."

Or he might simply have eaten the apple.

What about Alexander Fleming (1881-1955)? Many a scientist before him had seen green mold on a slide that he wanted to study, and, in disgust, had bawled out his technician and thrown the slide away. This mold thing was distracting. It spoiled the plan of operations. Fleming, however, was fascinated. Why was the area near the mold all *clear*? What happened to the colony of germs there?

Michael Faraday, too, was that sort of a scientist. And, as a matter of fact, he discovered exactly the opposite of the effect which Oersted noted. Faraday discovered that *magnetism can produce electricity*.

144

Here is how this effect can easily be demonstrated: A bar magnet is brought endwise into a coil of wire that is connected to an instrument, a galvanometer, and the galvanometer shows that the current has begun to flow.

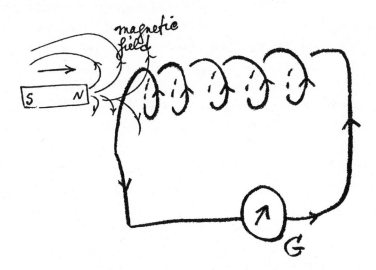

The current flows until the bar magnet no longer moves. Remember, there is no battery here. Yet, we get electricity.

If the bar magnet is pulled back out of the coil, we again get a current. But this time the current flows in the opposite direction.

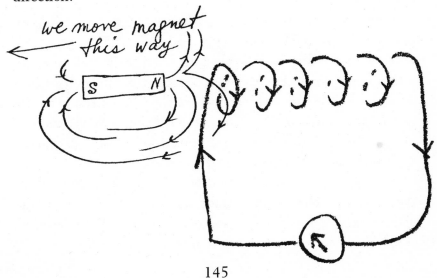

This experiment is only one example of the extensive research and discovery of Michael Faraday. He had something out of the ordinary in him, from the very beginning.

When Michael Faraday was a boy, the son of a blacksmith, he worked as an apprentice to a bookbinder. Yet he did more than bind books—he read them. His mind was searching, seeking answers to all sorts of questions. He became interested in science and began to perform experiments, especially experiments in chemistry.

For a number of years, Michael worked as a bookbinder. All the while he carried on with his self-education, and continued to experiment. For example, he studied the effect of an electrical current in passing through chemical solutions. By such means he was able to dissociate magnesium sulfate.

One day, in 1812, when a customer offered him some tickets to hear a series of lectures by the eminent scientist Sir Humphry Davy (1778-1829), Faraday eagerly accepted. He had long wanted to meet the famous scientist.

Humphry Davy, lecturing at the Royal Institution, was a spectacular educator who put on a striking show with a great deal of chemical apparatus in action. The young Faraday was entranced. He sat tense, eager. He took in everything, making hurried notes as he listened.

After each lecture, at home, Michael Faraday worked up the notes, expanded upon them, and made illustrations. He wrote up the fourth and last lecture, then bound all his notes into a book. Young Faraday sent the book to Humphry Davy, along with a request—a request that he be of some service to the great scientist. He would do anything, however menial. Perhaps he could wash bottles or repair laboratory equipment. He would even sweep the floor.

At first Davy advised Michael Faraday not to quit his skilled trade. Through his trade as a bookbinder, he could always earn a living. A laboratory assistant, Davy warned, could never be sure of steady employment. Besides, the pay

146

was poor, and there was little opportunity for advancement. Then, too, Faraday had had very little formal education. Moreover, Davy already had a laboratory assistant. There really was nothing for Faraday to do.

Faraday was not discouraged. He let it be known that he could wait until an opening turned up. The low pay and the insecurity didn't disturb him. Meanwhile, Davy himself was impressed. A great scientist, as we have observed, readily detects the unusual. Forced to dismiss his former assistant, Davy in time called upon Michael Faraday. He realized that an unusual and inspired youth had crossed his path.

Young Faraday, age twenty-one, went to work with a leap and a bound. From this day on, his role in life was clear to him: He was to be one of those persons who constantly seek to understand the secrets of nature.

Years later, when some asked Davy, "What was your greatest discovery?" he replied, "Michael Faraday."

(Still, when Michael Faraday became a candidate for election to the prestigious scientific body, the Royal Society, Humphry Davy tried very hard to prevent his election. Can you guess why? Nevertheless, Faraday was elected.)

As an assistant to Davy, Faraday accompanied the famous scientist on a five-month tour of scientific institutions of France, Italy, and Switzerland. Upon his return to England, the eager assistant was more than ever inspired to work in science, so in addition to helping Davy, he became increasingly engaged in researches of his own.

In 1825, Michael Faraday succeeded Davy as Director of the Laboratory at the Royal Institution. In swift succession came his wonderful discoveries in chemistry and physics.

We have already spoken about Faraday's discovery that, when the strength of a magnetic effect changes through a coil, electricity begins to flow. The magnetic effect, however, does not have to be the result of a magnet. After all, Oersted had found that electricity produces magnetism, so the follow-

147

ing arrangement should work: let the magnetic field of the coil of circuit *A* approach the coil of circuit *B*. Does current begin to flow in *B*? It does.

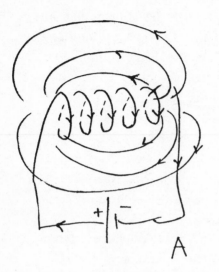

A

B

And what about moving *B* toward *A*? That is equally as effective. Well, then, how about having *A* and *B* close to each other like this:

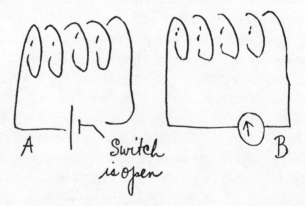

A

Switch is open

B

If we close the switch in *A*, what will happen? A magnetic field will come into existence, and some of it will penetrate the coil of *B*. Then will a current flow in circuit *B*? It will.

148

Faraday made investigations of this type also with coils wound on iron, and obtained much stronger fields because the iron became magnetized and gave magnetic lines of its own.

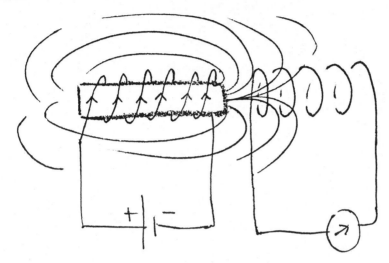

He experimented also with "breaking" a circuit after a strong magnetic field had been established.

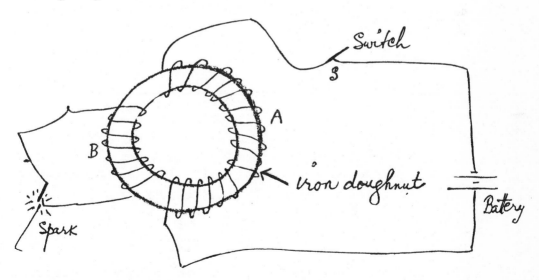

What happens? As the switch S opens, the magnetic lines collapse and cut across the turns of the coil B, inducing a momentary surge of current. A spark may actually appear at the switch blades. Faraday used a bit of carbon to make the spark more visible.

In England a few years ago, at the Royal Institution, I saw the coil with which Michael Faraday first drew out a spark.[1] The Institution has preserved also his laboratory, and much of the apparatus that he built, along with the equipment that he used. The Curator of the Royal Institution told me that during the Nazi bombings of London, Michael Faraday's coil and other apparatus were taken to the countryside and carefully hidden. Wars may come, the British knew, and wars may go, but the great works of man must go on.

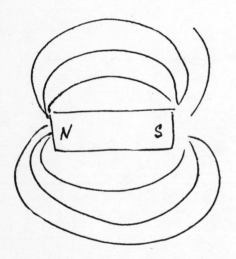
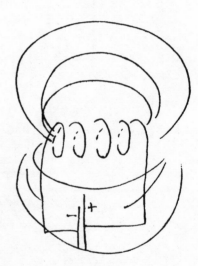

Incidentally, we were speaking of using the field of a bar magnet or the field from a coil which is connected to a battery. Do you happen to know that no one has yet been able to discover any difference between the two sets of magnetic fields?

---

[1]Here are Faraday's words on this matter: "By using charcoal at the ends of the B helix, a minute *spark* could be perceived when the contact of the battery with A was completed. . . ."

Thus, if you cover each set-up with a black cloth, and try exploring with a compass, you won't know which field results from the magnet and which results from the coil.

(I have a feeling there exists a basic difference, but no one has ever found any. Maybe you will?)

The coil and iron studies naturally led to investigations of this kind:

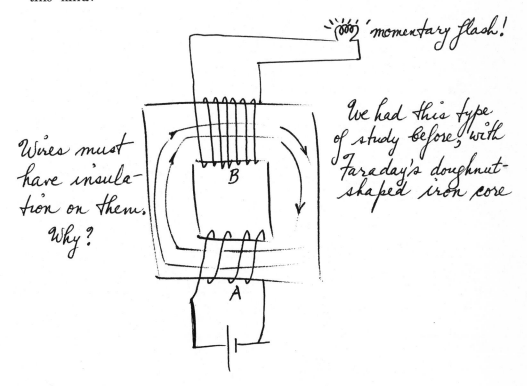

momentary flash!

We had this type of study before, with Faraday's doughnut-shaped iron core

Wires must have insulation on them. Why?

If we close the switch in the "Primary" circuit *A*, magnetic lines course through the iron, around the corner, and directly *through* the "Secondary" circuit *B*. But this induces a current in circuit *B*, and the lamp flashes on! Then it goes out. Why? Because the magnetic field becomes stable and steady—no longer changing.

If, however, we open the switch again, the magnetic lines collapse through the coil and we get another kick of a current. And so another flash.

If we take hold of the switch and start flipping it on, off, on, off, on . . . all day, the light will keep flashing. A more effective way to keep the light on is to connect an automatic switching mechanism, or, an alternating current generator. Faraday's work eventually led to this:

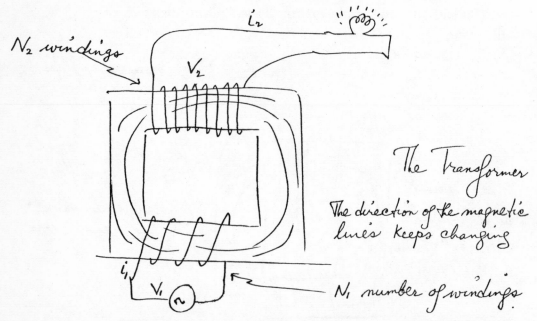

The voltage V_2 that appears across the secondary winding is greater than V_1, the voltage which applied to the primary winding, if N_2 is greater than N_1. Why? Because every turn of N_2 is cut by the coursing magnetic lines, and a larger grand total of cutting of lines is experienced by the secondary if it has more turns.

Thus,

$$\frac{V_2}{V_1} = \frac{N_2}{N_1}$$

What about the current that flows? It transforms like this:

$$\frac{i_2}{i_1} = \frac{N_1}{N_2}$$

Can you tell why?

A transformer today might handle 10,000 volts across the primary. But only 100 volts would appear in the secondary for use in a house. But i_2 is likely to be about 1 ampere. So how much·was i_1? The answer is .01 ampere. A high-voltage transformer takes on high alternating voltage at low current (an efficient combination for bringing the electricity from the power house) and transforms it to lower voltage but higher current, which is the combination we need for lamps, toasters, heaters, electric irons, and TV sets tuned to WTTW or other educational TV stations.

Michael Faraday worked on this problem, too:

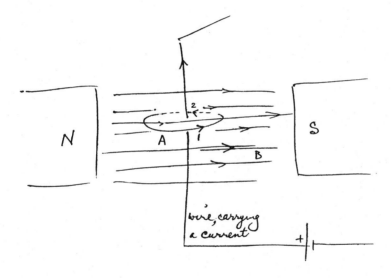

In the diagram, *above*, A are magnetic lines created by the current, and B are the magnetic lines created by the magnetic poles. At places closest to us, such as 1, the two sets of magnetic lines run the same way (to the right), and so they produce a net stronger magnetic field.

At places farther from us, such as 2, the magnetic lines of the wire run *opposite* to those of the magnet poles, so the field is weakened. In such a situation, *the wire moves* from the stronger region to the weaker.

Michael Faraday tried to make the motion *continue*. Perhaps the wire would spin on its axis. He was working toward an electric motor. Today we have such motors. Can you sketch one and explain how it works?

Of course, we can make an electrical *generator,* too, by spinning a coil between magnet poles.

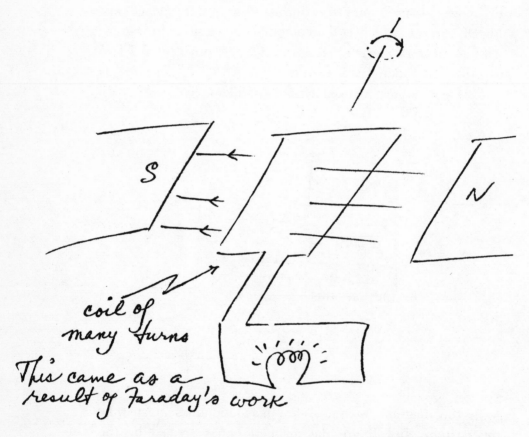

coil of
many turns

This came as a
result of Faraday's work

We spin the coil by hand, or by water power. As the coil turns, the number of lines penetrating keeps changing. Electricity is induced, and the lamp lights up. If we spin the coil fast enough, the lamp remains lit. The lamp, as shown, would have to rotate with the coil, and this is a bit ridiculous. How would you modify the circuit so that the lamp would not have to move?

We mentioned Michael Faraday's work in which he made electricity flow through chemical solutions. Let us consider a set-up which is easy to assemble in a laboratory, and which illustrates Faraday's basic laws of *electrolysis*—chemical changes produced by electricity.

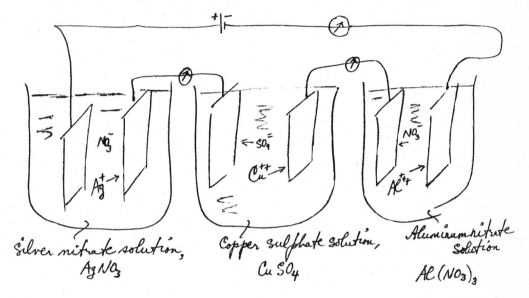

Silver nitrate solution, $AgNO_3$ Copper sulphate solution, $CuSO_4$ Aluminium nitrate Solution $Al(NO_3)_3$

1. First, let me say this: Every ammeter, or current-reading instrument, reads the *same*. Why? Because we can't lose electrical particles starting, say, from the negative side of the battery. They all will arrive at the positive side.

2. The number of charges which pass any point on the wire in, say, one second is therefore the same and this is identical to the number of charges which pass any point even in the solutions.

3. The number of *ions* (such as Ag^+, Cu^{++}, Al^{+++}) that pass through their respective cells and arrive at any relatively negative plate is *not* the same. Why not? Because the number of *charges*, as we said, has to be the same. Thus, if 60 Ag^+ make the trip, then only 30 Cu^{++} make the trip, and only 20 Al^{+++} make the trip. In each case, we will have 60 charges coursing through each cell.

Have you looked at a periodic chart (*see* Chapter 16, DMITRI MENDELEYEV, and Chapter 17, HENRY MOSELEY)? Well, 108 grams of silver, consisting of 6×10^{23} silver atoms, become 6×10^{23} Ag$^+$ in solution; and one gram of H, consisting of 6×10^{23} hydrogen atoms become 6×10^{23} H$^+$ in solution.

So it is possible to put many grams of silver into solution, pass a current, time the process, and wait until 108 grams of silver deposit onto the negative plate. We then have 6×10^{23} + charges arriving (each one having been brought by a silver ion, Ag$^+$).

From the reading of the ammeter and the time of flow, we calculate the amount of electrical quantity that was involved in the transfer of 6×10^{23} + charges. It comes out 96,500 coulombs (one coulomb is the quantity of electricity that passes when one ampere flows for one second). Therefore, Faraday was able to calculate the strength of *one* single +, by simply dividing as follows:

$$\frac{96,500}{6 \times 10^{23}}$$

He obtained the charge per ion, or coulombs for a single +.

Imagine, measuring the electrical strength of the + of a single atom!

Michael Faraday, despite his preoccupations with scientific problems of great importance, found time to give special lectures to children. His *Christmas Lectures* are still remembered today. He was happily married, but had no children of his own.

There is much more to the work of Michael Faraday.

For example, he studied "electrical fish" such as the electric eel, the torpedo fish, and the Gymnotus. He put his hands into the water, touched the fish, and received many shocks. He measured the strength of their electrical kick.

Amazingly enough, he found that the head of a Gymnotus was like the positive side of a battery and the tail was like the negative end.

He had the Gymnotus in a shallow tank of water, once, and threw in a small fish to see what would happen. Faraday wondered if the Gymnotus knew about its own electrical powers. In a split second, the Gymnotus coiled itself around the little fish and shot an electrical charge right through it. The little fish died at once, and the Gymnotus ate it.

Many such experiments, as well as experiments on electricity in the air, convinced Faraday that all electricity is the same, whether it comes from the atmosphere, the chemicals of batteries, or the bodies of living things.

One of the most exciting investigations was that of looking for an electrical field inside of a charged metallic cage.

entire framework has been charged.

Would there be an electrical field at an interior point P? Faraday found that there was no field anywhere inside! The various parts of the cage with their charges cancel out in their effects at any point P. It is easier to see the reason with a spherical cage:

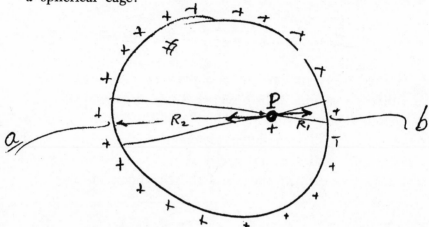

The charge on the portion of the sphere *a* repels a test charge at *P*, to the right. The charge on the portion *b* repels the test charge to the left. These two forces cancel out. The portion *a* has more charge than has *b*, but is farther away. And the effects just cancel.

We can think of the cage as shielding the people and instruments inside, because, if there is electricity on the way from the outside, it will get only as far as the cage. The cage will become charged, but nothing will be felt inside.

This ought to remind us that, during a lightning storm, an automobile is a safe place, because the inside is shielded. During one of our wars, by the way, I worked for several years in a cage! I was working on sensitive measurements in connection with the radar project at the MIT Radiation Laboratory. We did not want the instruments to be disturbed by any kind of external electrical effect, such as the radio-type waves produced by other scientists working near-by.

The frame of the cage can have, actually, a fairly large mesh (sizes of openings) if you are protecting the inside from long waves. In my case, the mesh was small, because I wanted to be shielded from short external waves as well as from long ones.

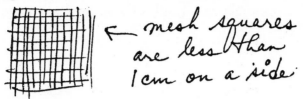

mesh squares are less than 1 cm on a side.

There are radar waves which are of rather short wave length, like this:

and even smaller. Lightning produces a burst of longer waves. Ordinary radio waves are one meter or more in wave length.

wave-length is distance between any two corresponding points

A   B

A wave length is the distance between any two corresponding points in the advance of a wave, such as from A to B, *above.*

Michael Faraday did not always succeed. One of his most exciting hunches did not prove out. He wanted to see if electricity and gravity were related. He guessed that an ordinary neutral weight, such as a rock, when in motion might produce an electrical effect. So he dropped many kinds of weights through coils of wire—but no current was ever produced.

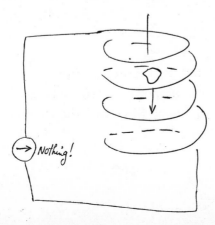

Nothing!

Is this the final word on this question? I doubt it.

We must not forget just one more fascinating experiment that is now possible as a result of Faraday's pioneering work:

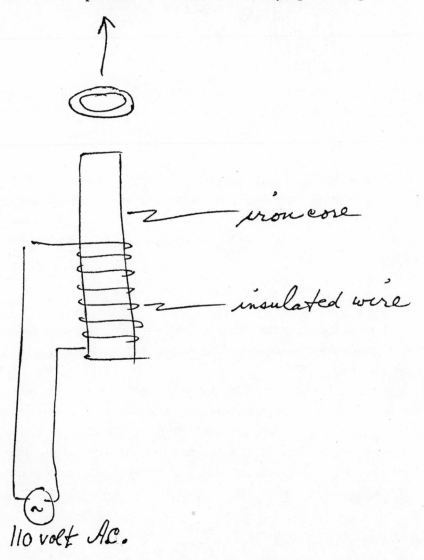

iron core

insulated wire

110 volt A.C.

Wind an insulated coil over an iron core. Connect the apparatus to a source of power (110 volts or household current). Now, drop a metal ring over the iron core. The ring will fly away!

Why does this happen? The magnetic lines from the iron and coil induce a current in the ring. The current flows in such a way as to give the bottom of the ring the same magnetic polarity as the end of the coil and wire. Thus, repulsion occurs.

and when the line current reverses (remember, A.C.), then

(Side view)

In his later years, Faraday was sick much of the time. He began to lose his memory. Then he turned his work over to younger men, men who first had to stand on his shoulders before they could advance the cause of science.

Acclaim came to Faraday from all over the world. The scientists of Great Britain wanted him to be the president of their societies. Even to the highest learned bodies, however, he shook his head.

"I must always remain just plain Michael Faraday," he said to them. "Right to the end."

The end came on August 25, 1867. Yet, to this day, there is a statue of a youth at the portals of the Royal Institution in London. Above the statue is carved an inscription which reads that, in 1812, the youth Michael Faraday was present in those halls to attend a series of four lectures on science.

Maxwell

13

James Clerk Maxwell

1831-1879

In school they called him "Dafty." And, in schools today,
children often call a boy "Dafty," or usually "Daffy." Children
call a boy "Dafty" or "Daffy" because he is "different." Perhaps he speaks in an unusual manner, or wears "funny"
clothes.

James Clerk Maxwell did talk in a strange way—he was
shy and hesitant, and he answered questions in a round-
about manner. Also, he did look strange, for he wore clothes
that his father had designed for him, his mother having died
when he was only nine years old. In private, he had a tutor
who often hit him and pulled his ears. But, from pride, he
refused to complain to his father. Instead, he became shy and
hesitant in his speech.

He laughed a puzzling, ironic laugh. This his school
fellows could not fathom. So they began to call him other
names—they called him "idiot." From abusive words they
went on to abusive acts. They shoved him and hit him.
Driven to desperation, this strange boy occasionally grew
wild with fury. He rushed at his tormentors, fighting like a
demon. He was, however, outnumbered.

(Isaac Newton, you recall, also had been tormented. Once,
in retaliation, he flew at a big bully. With flying fists, he
whipped the bruiser and sent him running. This triumph
liberated Newton from his fears and excessive shyness.)

Maxwell, too, in time, proved superior to the bullies who
annoyed him. By the age of thirteen, this shy Scottish boy
was building splendid geometrical solids and mathematical
models. He knew all the theory about them. The following

year, furthermore, he won a medal for mathematics and a prize for verse that he had written.

James Maxwell's father was alert to the boy's flowering abilities. He took the lad to many scientific meetings. So affected was James by the presence of the scientists and by their discussions that he plunged with burning enthusiasm into further scientific studies.

At the age of fifteen, James prepared a scholarly scientific report on unusual ovals and how to sketch them. A professor presented this paper to the eminent Royal Institution. At sixteen, James was off to Edinburgh University, still seemingly eccentric, but fully launched on a life of science.

Religious feeling played an important role in Maxwell's life, and to his formal Christian religion he added something of his own—a rapport with all humanity, a religion of universal sympathy. When he was a young professor, he lectured to working men in Cambridge on ethical, aesthetic, and philosophical subjects.

Maxwell had become a very handsome man, with a noble head, black glowing eyes, and a black beard. He had sensitive, expressive features—a poetic look. His skin, however, was sallow, perhaps because he cared little for exercise or sports, though he was a good swimmer. Of medium height, Maxwell had a strong build. He walked with a spring to his step.

All of his life he remained a quiet, reserved man, seldom laughing, though his eyes twinkled at times in response to a merry situation. Humility remained a dominant characteristic of his personality. When traveling in public conveyance, he would choose to go by third class in order to be with the good common people. (The great Russian scientist Mendeleyev, whenever he rode in a train, also went by third class, for the same reason.)

James Maxwell married a woman who was sympathetic to his scholarly ways, and who even helped him in his home laboratory experiments. These experiments ranged all over the map of physics and even touched upon astronomy. He worked on optics, particularly the theory of color; he worked on mechanics and gyroscopic motion; he investigated all sorts of problems in electricity after having carefully studied the published researches of Michael Faraday.

The planet Saturn drew his attention because a prize had been offered for the best solution to this problem: Are the rings of Saturn *solid* or are they made of countless separate particles all orbiting around the planet? In a beautiful mathematical exposition, Maxwell gave the answer and won the famous Adams prize.

(John Couch Adams was the young British scientist who had predicted the existence of a planet beyond Uranus, the planet which became known as Neptune. To be fair, we should mention that the Frenchman Leverrier also predicted the existence of a planet beyond Uranus. We'll consider Adams and Leverrier later.)

Maxwell's theoretical findings about Saturn's rings were these: a uniform solid ring could not be stable. A *loaded* solid ring would be stable, but only if the loading were about 82 per cent on one side and 18 per cent on the other.

between 17 and 19% of the mass of the ring

between 81 and 83% of the mass

If a ring were loaded in any other manner, it would be destroyed by a collision between its inside edge and the surface of Saturn. The rings, of course, could scarcely be expected to have been loaded accidentally in such a precise manner—82 per cent and 18 per cent. For this reason, Maxwell concluded that the rings must be made of separate particles, whether solid or liquid.

Thirty-eight years later, Professor Keeler showed, by spectroscopic study, that the inner portions of the rings revolve more quickly than the outer ones, and that this could not possibly hold true for a solid ring. Why not?

Some astronomers now believe the particles are snowballs with grit or dust in them. Other scientists believe the particles to be ice crystals.

Maxwell went on from the study of the myriads of particles of Saturn's rings to the myriads of particles of a gas—the atoms.

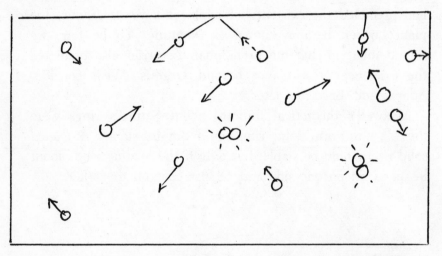

Box with gas, atoms moving at great speeds

Maxwell tried to calculate the speeds at which the atoms move. He knew, of course, that they would move faster than otherwise if the box is heated, and the temperature is raised. Yet, he was interested in a more subtle point: do the atoms all move with the same speeds? No, he knew, this could not be, since the atoms collide at random with each other and with the walls of the container. There must be a "distribution of velocities," and Maxwell found it, by theoretical analysis.

He then calculated the velocity of molecules in air at 60° F. to be 1,505 feet per second, and that an average molecule experiences about 500,000 collisions per inch. He also calculated that one molecule experiences 8,077,200,000 collisions per second. Today, scores of years later, with all our refined techniques, these values are still close to what is considered right.

Maxwell, imbued with a fine scientific sense, could examine any problems, even social and political ones, without prejudice. (Einstein, too, was able to do this to a remarkable degree, perhaps because his thoughts for nearly all his life were "up there," among the stars and galaxies and in space and time and space-time.)

Maxwell's wife made a good home for him, and for his dog Tobi—a dog who seemed to share his discoveries and who helped make his life more tolerable. Maxwell, however, worked too hard, and felt ill and hard-pressed too often, though the pressure largely was self-imposed. Accordingly, one day, he resigned his professorship—at the age of thirty-five—and retired to his country home, gratefully relieved of the responsibility of teaching classes, though he continued his theoretical researches.

Yet this liberation did not last. Six years later, in 1871, he returned to Cambridge, to the University, to establish a physics laboratory which was to be named in honor of another "funny" or "Dafty" scientist, the gifted man, Henry Cavendish (1731-1810).

Perhaps the most remarkable of James Maxwell's many scientific contributions resulted from his investigation of the basic electrical and magnetic discoveries of his time. Let us summarize the important findings in electricity and magnetism, and then we shall see what a remarkable achievement he brought about.

1. It was known that positive and negative charges could exist separately and that they attract each other, presumably reaching for one another with invisible "electric lines."

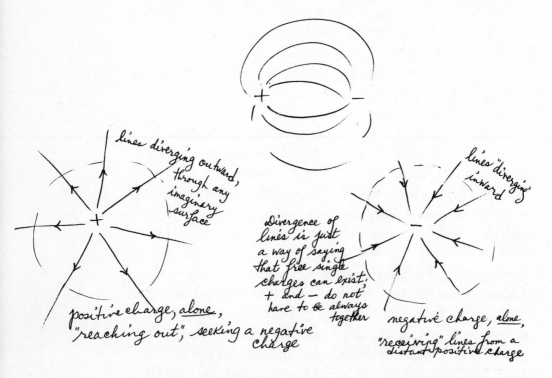

lines diverging outward, through any imaginary surface

positive charge, alone, "reaching out", seeking a negative charge

Divergence of lines is just a way of saying that free single charges can exist; + and − do not have to be always together

lines "diverging" inward

negative charge, alone, "receiving" lines from a distant positive charge

2. *Magnetic* poles, on the other hand, did not exist separately. (A few scientists in recent years have claimed that they have found N and S *separates*, but this has not been generally confirmed.)

We say that for magnetic lines there is no *net* divergence. This is just a way of saying N and S come in pairs.

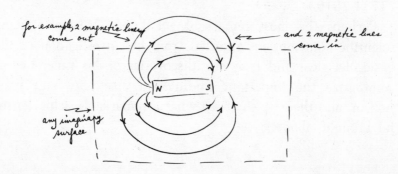

for example, 2 magnetic lines come out

and 2 magnetic lines come in

any imaginary surface

In general, it is enough just to make the familiar sketch:

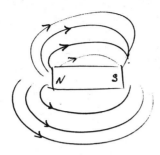

3. You recall that Michael Faraday had found that if there is a change in the number of magnetic lines that "flow" into a coil—or out of it—electricity begins to flow in the coil.

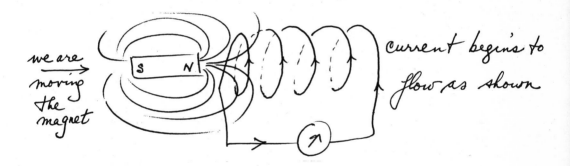

we are moving the magnet

current begins to flow as shown

This is "electromagnetic induction."

4. The Danish scientist, Hans Christian Oersted (1777-1851), had found in 1820 that, when an electrical current flows, a magnetic field is produced.

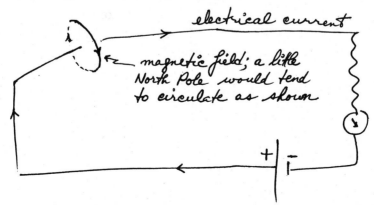

electrical current

magnetic field; a little North Pole would tend to circulate as shown

+ −

This current is presumably a current of electrical *particles*, and we call it a "conduction current." Today we believe that actually the flow is in the opposite direction and consists of *electrons,* or tiny negative charges.

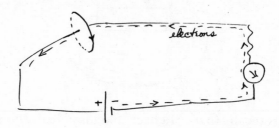

Maxwell, however, felt that there was more to this fourth item. He had a hunch that we ought to get a magnetic field not only when charged particles were flowing, as in a wire, but even when they did not actually flow through a space. Here is what we mean:

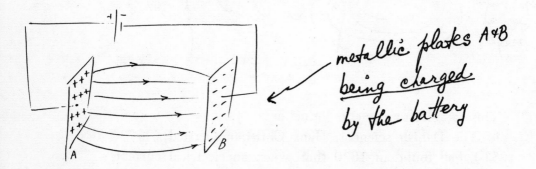

metallic plates A & B
being charged
by the battery

As the charges begin to appear on the plates, electric lines begin to reach across from, say, plate *A* to plate *B*. Remember how we drew such lines before?

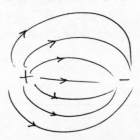

Now, as the lines increase in number, because of the charging up of the plates, we have electric lines pulsing through space. Does this remind you of anything? In item 3, in Faraday's discovery, we have *magnetic* lines pulsing through space—through the space enclosed by a coil of wire:

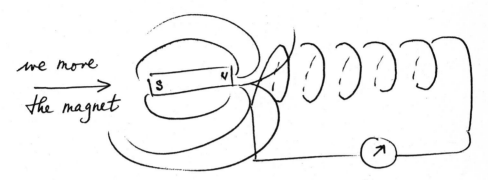

And what happened? An *electrical* flow began to occur. As a matter of fact, the coil is not absolutely necessary. If magnetic lines simply pulse through *any* space, an electrical effect is created around the magnetic pulse.

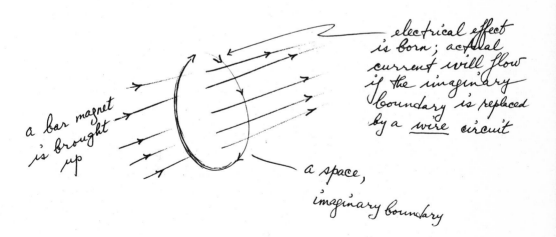

Maxwell then reasoned that when the *electric lines* pulse through a space—such as that between the two metallic plates or any space at all—a *magnetic effect* should come into existence around the pulsing electric lines.

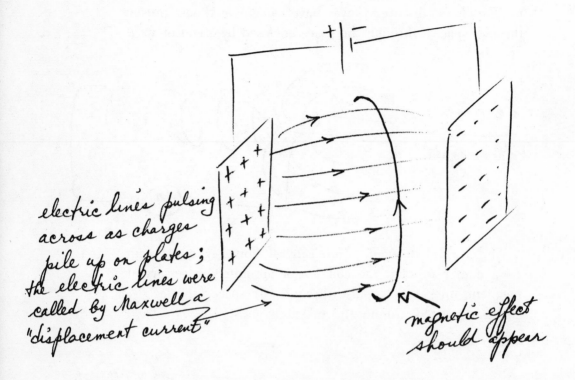

electric lines pulsing across as charges pile up on plates; the electric lines were called by Maxwell a "displacement current"

magnetic effect should appear

Remember that this effect is in addition to the magnetic effect produced if we have real charged *particles* moving. Yet, we don't need a flow of charged particles, or *conduction current,* to produce the magnetic field. We can get a magnetic field from the mere pulsing of electric lines through space. That is, we can get magnetic lines from a change in the displacement current. (Maxwell called the electric lines a *displacement current.*)

So said the Dafty James Clerk Maxwell. And we'll examine in a moment the result of these findings and of the theory put forward by Maxwell. Let us first summarize the problem by a sketch, in order to understand exactly what Maxwell was about to tackle.

①

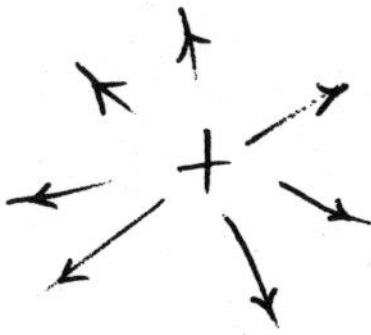

arrows give direction in which a + charge dropped anywhere would move

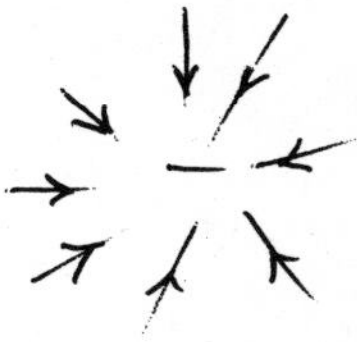

here, too, arrows give direction in which a + charge dropped anywhere would move

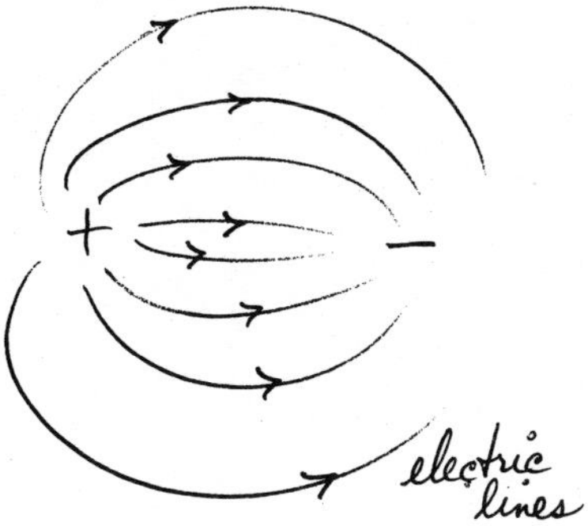

+ and —

"reach" for each other

electric lines

②

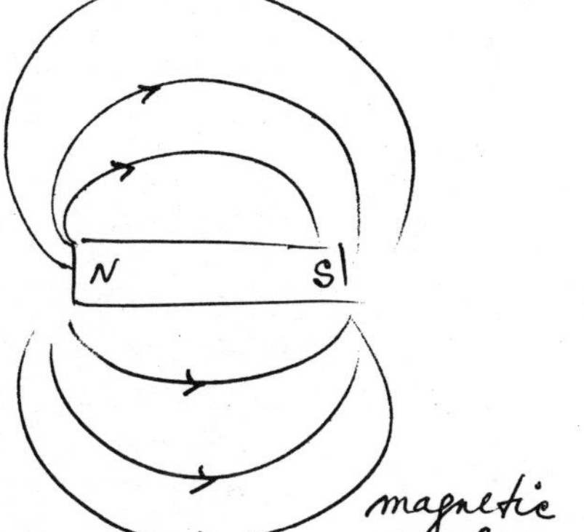

No free N and S poles — separate — exist

magnetic lines

(3)

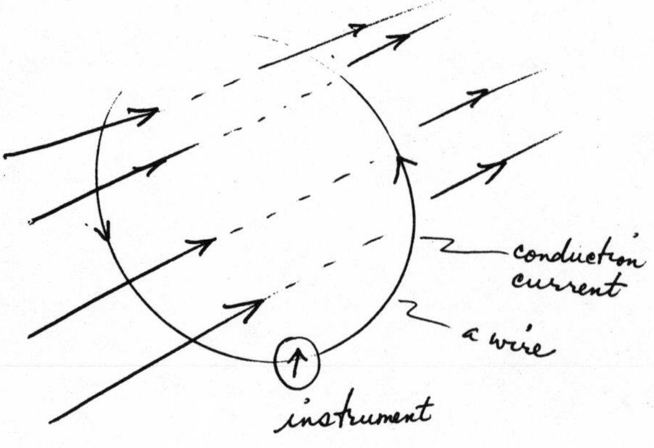

conduction
current

a wire

instrument

magnetic
lines are here
pulsing through
the space
bounded by a
wire, pro-
ducing thereby
actual cur-
rent flow

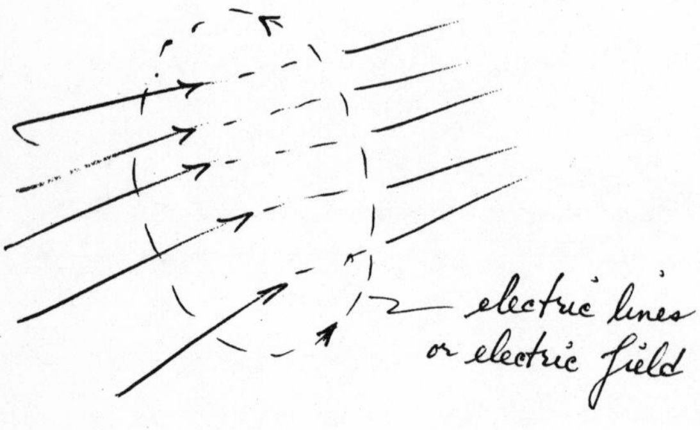

electric lines
or electric field

magnetic lines pulsing
through a mere space,
produce an electrical
burst of lines, but not
an actual flow of
charged particles

(4)

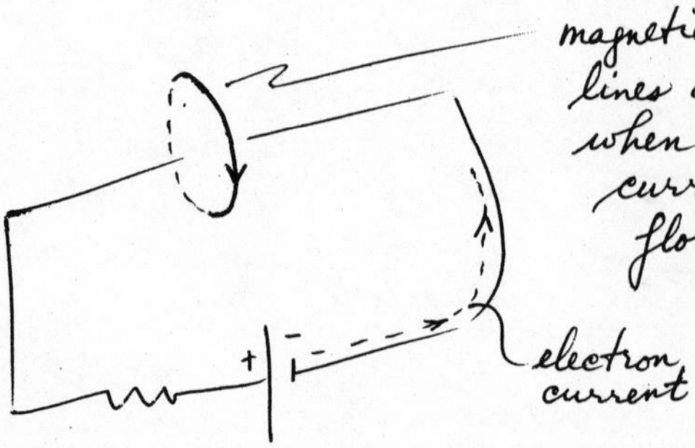

magnetic field, or magnetic
lines or loops are produced
when an actual conduction
current (charged particles)
flows

electron
current

And Maxwell's inspired addition to item 4,

electric lines pulsing through a mere space, produce a magnetic effect around them

displacement current

Maxwell put all of these discoveries and his theory into mathematical form. He then asked himself these questions: What is the consequence of all this? What conclusions must follow?

His problem is equivalent to saying, "A man is three times as old as his son. The ages of the father and son add up to sixty. What is the consequence of these two statements? What conclusions must follow?"

Well, this is an easy one: The father is forty-five, and the son is fifteen. That's the final conclusion. It *does* follow inevitably from our two statements. We say in mathematics that we have solved the two equations (statements) simultaneously. Thus, Maxwell essentially solved the mathematical items we have been considering simultaneously. And what was the result?

He obtained this result: Electric and magnetic waves should exist, able to travel through air or empty space, with a speed equal to the speed of light!

How about that? A man predicts electromagnetic waves traveling through space.

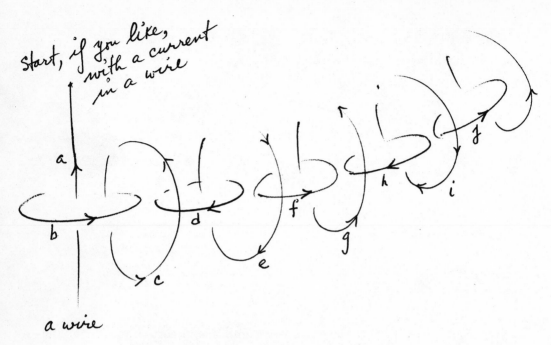

a wire

Let us start with a current in a wire. The current *a* moves through the wire. *a* gives rise to the magnetic line *b*. *b* then produces *c; c* produces *d; d* generates *e; e* gives rise to *f*. *b, d, f, h*, and *j* are magnetic lines, or loops. *c, e, g*, and *i* are electric lines, or loops.

If the current in the wire reverses, as in alternating current, then all the loops have arrows going in opposite directions.

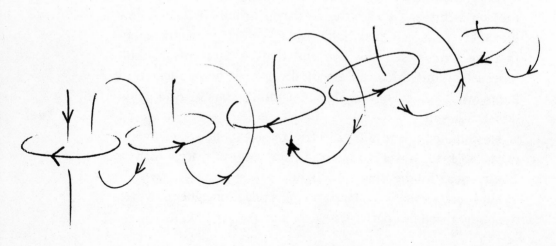

The two sets of loops are perpendicular to each other. And we could draw the "waves" together in this manner:

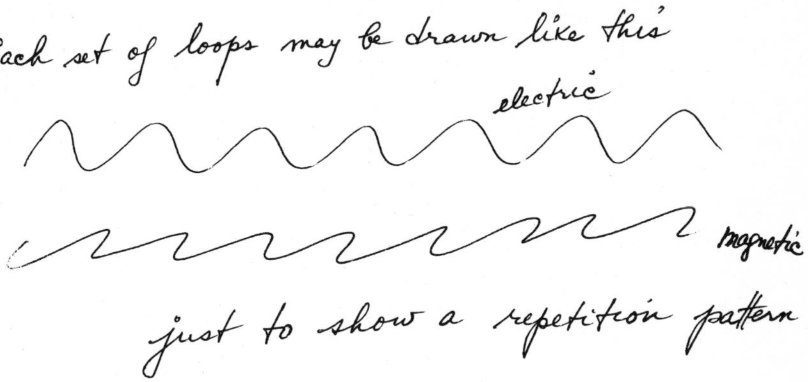

Each set of loops may be drawn like this

electric

magnetic

just to show a repetition pattern

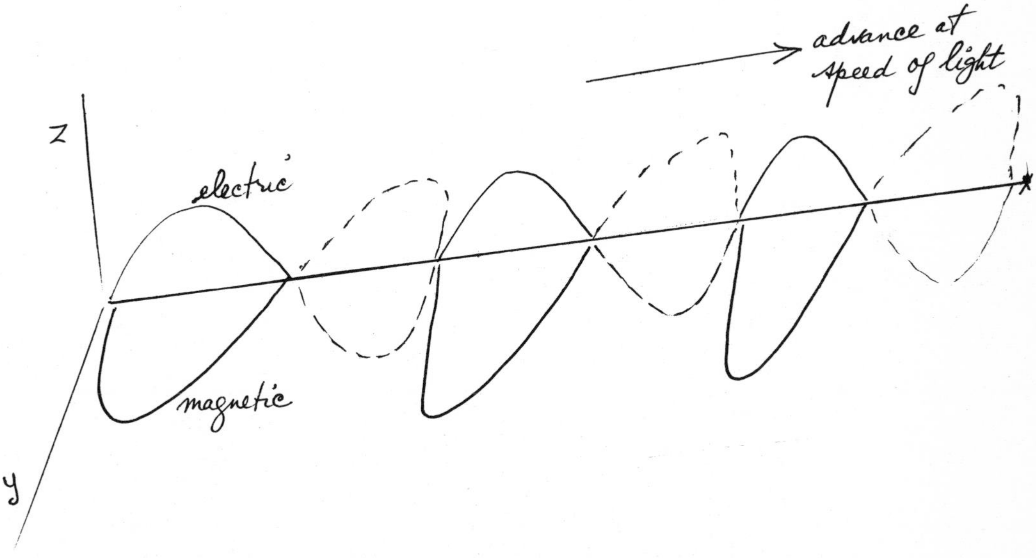

advance at speed of light

Z

electric

magnetic

y

Here, of course, we are trying to show the electric waves in the vertical plane (ZX) and the magnetic waves in the horizontal plane (XY).

Do such waves really exist?

Scientists pondered this question in Maxwell's time.

Years later, the scientist Heinrich Hertz (1857-1894) discovered that the Maxwell waves actually exist, and can be created in the laboratory. Then came Marchese Guglielmo Marconi (1874-1937), radio waves, and, later, television waves. It was all true. What Maxwell had predicted came to be verified.

Maxwell had declared also that light itself was of an electromagnetic nature. And this assertion was confirmed.

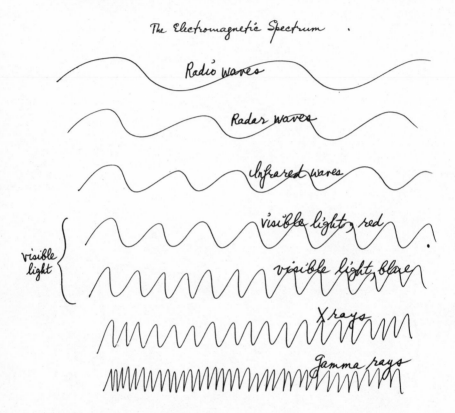

The Electromagnetic Spectrum

Radio waves

Radar waves

Infrared waves

visible light, red

visible
light

visible light, blue

X rays

Gamma rays

Maxwell's electromagnetic waves of the radio type may one day put us into touch with other worlds. Such waves have already been bounced off the moon, making the round trip in 2.4 seconds. They have been bounced off Mars, off Venus, and off the sun.

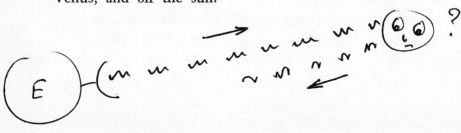

One day a message may reach us from outer space, from an inhabited or "Good Earth" of some sun.

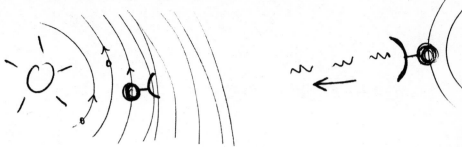

We are searching for such messages. And I am sure that Maxwell type waves are being used now for communication among many Good Earths in space, for the universe is immense, solar systems must be many in number, and Good Earths must be innumerable.

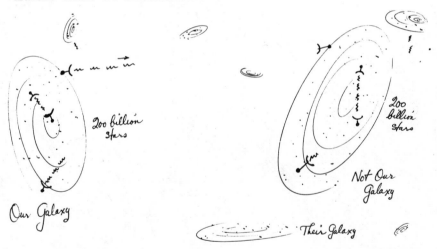

Of the search for messages from other worlds, James Clerk Maxwell knew nothing. He did not even know that his waves, which he discovered on paper, were later actually discovered. For, on November 5, 1879, the once-tormented schoolboy died.

He was shy, and hesitant about speaking. But he has brought his fellow Earthlings to the verge of conversation with the entire universe.

Leverrier

Adams and Leverrier

1819-1892, 1811-1877

The planet Uranus was misbehaving. It wasn't moving in its orbit according to expectations. It had been moving too fast for some years, and then it began to move too slowly.

Uranus had been discovered by William Herschel, you will recall, with the help of his sister, Caroline. Astronomers followed this planet in its motion for a long time. They calculated its speed and its orbit around the sun. To the observers' amazement, Uranus wasn't playing ball according to the rules.

By the year 1840, it was off course by 1.5 minutes of arc.

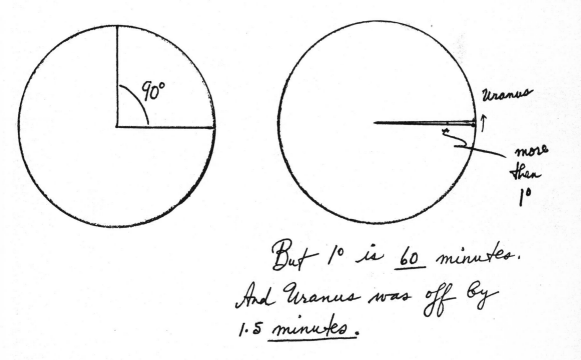

But 1° is 60 minutes.
And Uranus was off by
1.5 minutes.

Of course, Uranus was far away, so even 1.5 minutes of angle gave it quite a length of arc by which it was off schedule.

E ————————————————————————————————•

The astronomers were puzzled. What caused this strange behavior? Usually, problems of this sort involve the determination of an effect from a cause. For example, let's start with an object such as a comet or a planet. What we want to know is how this object will affect another object.

$A \overset{|}{\underset{\downarrow}{\bigcirc}}$ $\bigcirc\,^B$

In such a common problem, we make use of Newton's *Law of Universal Gravitation* to calculate how B perturbs A:

M_1 is Mass of A

M_2 is Mass of B

$$F = \frac{G\,M_1 \times M_2}{R^2}$$

Yet, in the case of the erratic behavior of Uranus, we have a far more difficult problem. We are given an *effect,* and we are to find the cause.

(Here is another problem of this type: There are thousands of asteroids, or planetoids, orbiting around the sun in the space between Mars and Jupiter. Where did they come from? We used to think that once upon a time there was a planet between Mars and Jupiter, and that this planet exploded. A Japanese scientist, however, has shown that one bursting planet could not possibly have accounted for all the asteroids and their motions. He has been making calculations and believes that *five* bursting planets could account for the asteroid belt. How did they burst? By overheating? By collisions? The problem is not yet satisfactorily solved.)

Astronomers were beginning to consider the possibility that Newton's law of gravity may not hold at large distances. That is, they suspected Uranus, at 1,800,000,000 miles, is so far away that the sun may not act upon it according to $F = \dfrac{GM_1M_2}{R^2}$. Therefore, astronomers would be wrong in predicting an orbit, according to Newton's formula.

Other astronomers speculated, "Though Newton's law is probably right, there may be some unknown comet acting upon Uranus."

Others spoke of an unseen planet.

In the year 1841, at Cambridge University in England, a third-year student, John Couch Adams, became interested in the problem. He decided to have a go at it as soon as he was graduated from the university. Here is what he wrote in his diary on July 3, 1841:

Formed a design, in the beginning of this week, of investigating, as soon as possible after taking my degree, the irregularities in the motion of Uranus, which are yet unaccounted for, in order to find whether they may be attributed to the action of an undiscovered planet beyond it, and, if possible, thence to determine approximately the elements of its orbit, etc.; which would probably lead to its discovery.

John Couch Adams was graduated in 1843 with top honors. He then took on the difficult mathematical problem of accounting for the errant ways of Uranus. In September 1845 Adams gave a stack of calculations to Professor Challis, astronomer at Cambridge.

What Adams was making known, in effect, with his calculations, was this: "If we point a powerful telescope at the place in the sky which I have calculated here, we'll find a new planet. That's what is tampering with the expected orbit of Uranus."

Challis advised Adams to write to Professor George Airy, Astronomer-Royal, at Greenwich. In October, Adams did write to Airy, sending along his mathematical document, with the clearly indicated suggestion, "If you point the telescope . . ." Adams gave precisely the point in the sky where one was to look.

Professor Airy sat frowning. True, Adams had graduated with highest honors, and he did send in all his calculations. Yet, Adams was a very young man. Moreover, the observatory had a program of sky study completely planned for weeks in advance. One could not upset one's plans every time some young man sent in a suggestion.

Airy did not point the telescope. Instead, he sent a letter to the young Adams, asking if his theory could explain not only the error in the *angular* position of Uranus, but also the error in the *distance* from the sun.

Adams was annoyed. He could readily answer "yes" to Airy's question, but why was all this time being wasted? All Airy had to do was to point the telescope. He had been given clear directions as to where to point it.

Professor Airy, failing to receive a reply from Adams, went through the ill-fated act—that of filing Adams' document. He relegated it to the sliding vault of frustrated hopes.

Meanwhile, back in France, a brilliant young mathematician (young, but still older than Adams) was asked by Professor Arago to tackle the problem of Uranus. The mathematician was Urbain Jean Joseph Leverrier.

On November 10, 1845—only a few days after Adams' document had reached Professor Airy—Leverrier had his first results concerning a possible new planet.

(We must remember that Adams and Leverrier worked independently. They did not know each other. They did not communicate. Neither of them was aware that anyone else was at work on the problem.)

Soon, by June 1, 1846, Leverrier had new results, more precise ones than previously, and these were published.

At about this time Adams decided to reply to Airy's letter. Airy, however, had received also a copy of Leverrier's publication, and he wrote to Leverrier asking the same questions that he had asked of Adams. Leverrier replied at once.

By this time, Professor Airy was impressed. The calculations of the two young men had been made independently, yet they were amazingly the same.

Accordingly, on July 9, 1846, Professor Airy asked Professor Challis to make a search with the telescope at his disposal—a telescope called the *Northumberland Equatorial.*

Challis agreed, and he soon began a leisurely sweep of the heavens—a series of sweeps, in fact, in the area indicated by the calculations of the two mathematicians. But he actually surveyed the region merely in the manner of "once over lightly."

The once-over-lightly method is usually not dependable in such matters. Remember, we have to look on one night (today we take photographs), then go back several times for further inspections on later nights—days, weeks, or possibly months later. Then, we compare the several views of the sky to detect whether or not any "dot" has moved!

Once-over-lightly is adequate only if we already have a map of the particular region of the sky. Challis had no such map. Accordingly, he could conclude nothing.

In France, meanwhile, Leverrier had become impatient with all this delaying. He had presented another report before the French Academy on August 31, 1846, and on this date there was yet no news from England, where existed

185

several fine telescopes. Consequently, on September 18, 1846, Leverrier sent his report and calculations to Dr. John Galle, who was Assistant Astronomer at Berlin. The papers arrived on September 23, 1846, and Galle went to his telescope, set it, and started to search. Within half an hour, he had found it.

How could he? How could he have come upon it in one look? Galle perceived a bright object only one degree off from Leverrier's position, and, he wondered, is this one of the stars that belongs there? Opening a drawer, he took out Bremiker's *Star Map*. The map displayed no dot corresponding to the bright object which had caught his eye. That being the case, the object was not a star! It was the planet. It was the predicted planet, whose existence two men had figured out on paper.

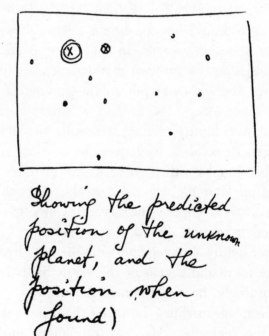

Showing the predicted position of the unknown planet, and the position when found)

The unknown planet became known, of course, as "Neptune," and soon a great deal of knowledge was determined about it. In the first place, here is how the planet had been affecting Uranus:

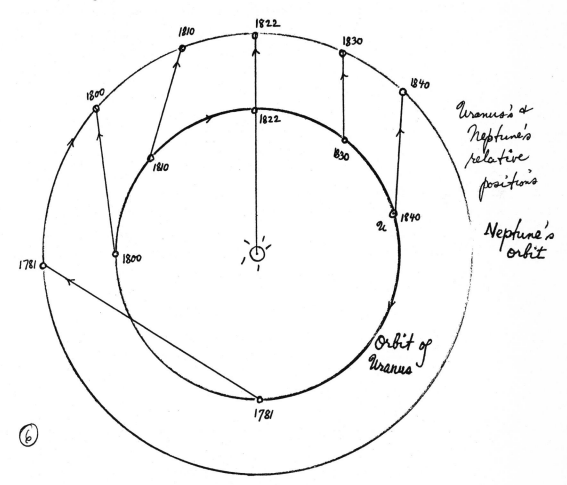

In 1822, Neptune only affects *distance* of Uranus from the Sun
Before 1822, Neptune had been *pulling* on Uranus to speed it along
After 1822,   "   " . " pulling "   "   to slow it down

As the diagram, *above,* indicates, before 1822, Neptune had been pulling on Uranus to speed it along. After 1822, Neptune had been pulling on Uranus to slow it down.

The planet Neptune is about 2,700,000,000 miles from the earth. It is 31,000 miles wide across its equator, and has a volume large enough to contain seventy-two earths! (Remember, volumes depend on the cube of the diameter; thus, if one sphere is four times as wide as another, it then has 64 times the volume.)

The mass of Neptune is 17 times that of earth, and its gravity is 12 per cent higher. It *rotates* once around in 15 hours, 40 minutes; and it takes 165 earth years to go once around the sun. If we ever land on Neptune, we'll need a speed of 14 miles per second to escape from it, on a one-shot firing, which is about 50,000 mph, or twice the velocity required to escape from earth.

However, we had better not land on Neptune. The planet has an atmosphere of the poisonous methane and ammonia. Hydrogen and helium, too, have been detected by the spectroscope. Nor would the temperature please us very much, since Neptune harbors a cool −300° F. One cannot expect to find life on this planet, although some theorists would like to qualify this statement by saying "life as we know it on earth."

Neptune has two moons, *Triton* being 3000 miles in diameter, which is almost 900 miles bigger than our moon.

Incidentally, Triton goes around Neptune the "wrong" way, or is *retrograde,* that is, backward, though I think that it is unfair to say it does so to commemorate Airy's work. He was actually an accomplished astronomer.

The second moon is *Nereid,* 200 miles in diameter.

We should note that news of Galle's discovery spread swiftly throughout Germany, France, and England. By the first day of October, Professor Challis and John Couch Adams at Cambridge had heard of the discovery. We can imagine how Adams felt. And Challis.

Englishmen began making claims that Adams had been the true discoverer, while Frenchmen, annoyed, replied that their man should be credited. Professor Arago maintained that the new planet should be named "Leverrier." As you know, however, this designation did not stick, and the planet was finally named Neptune, as though it were the God of the Heavenly Sea.

The friends of Adams and Leverrier fought on for years with their claims. The two scientists, I'm glad to report, remained largely *hors de combat.*

You'll be interested to know that Professor Challis checked his observations and found in his notes that he had seen Neptune on August 4 and on August 12, 1846, in a couple of his leisurely sweeps, but he had failed to identify it. The astronomer Lalande also had seen it, in 1795! He had, however, put it down as a star.

The ironic point to be made about Lalande's observation is this: He had seen the planet twice at Paris, once on May 8, 1795, and again on May 10. However, because the two position readings *did not agree,* he rejected one and placed a question mark after the other. That is the manner in which an ordinary scientist behaves. Remember?

An ordinary scientist lacks the confidence and the wit to accept an important phenomenon when it is thrust before his eyes. What might be a great discovery he regards as a mere distraction. Meanwhile, he settles back into his comfortable rut.

And what, through the years, became of John Couch Adams and Urbain Jean Joseph Leverrier? Both of them continued to perform as great astronomers and mathematicians for many years.

Leverrier, later in life, accepted an administrative post, where, I regret to say, he tried to govern men under him in a rigid, precise manner, which was appropriate for astronomical reckoning, but ill-suited to dealings with human beings. The men actually rose up against him. He would have done better to have remained in science, proper.

The hazard of the successful scientist is the temptation to accept posts of great "authority," with impressive titles, enticing salaries, and not too much to do with science.

Adams also was offered an administrative post. He, however, turned it down. Moreover, Adams was offered knighthood, but he declined this great honor, saying, "I am not wealthy enough to be a knight."

Both men had predicted the planet Neptune. Both should be regarded as discoverers. They did good work, and they left all of us the better for their having lived. They gave scientists a real boost in morale, for they bet their intellectual best that scientific laws could be relied upon and that men must dare to make use of them and to call the shots as they see them.

Kelvin

BROWN BROTHERS

15

Lord Kelvin

1824-1907

"Could it be that the universe might be running down?" a friend of mine asked recently, complaining that he had been staying awake nights, obsessed by this thought.

"Running down where?" I inquired, playing it cool so that he might relax.

"I heard that the sun may burst wide open," he confided. "It is thinking of exploding."

Now, this happens to be true. At least, from our present-day knowledge of the stars, we can conclude the sun may actually go *bang!* In about eight billion years, that is.

I explained this to my friend, in a casual manner.

"It will be a long time," I said, off-handedly.

"Will it happen suddenly?" he questioned me. "Or will we have some sort of warning?"

"Of course, we'll have a warning," I assured him. "Take it easy. We'll have a couple of hundred years' warning.

"The sun will grow hotter. And so will we. Finally, we'll decide to go to another planet that is much farther away from the sun. Maybe to Pluto. Many suns, or stars, explode with warning, you might say. They become novas. Others explode all at once—these are the supernovas. Our sun should become a nova."

He sat down and leaned toward me.

"What if you're wrong?" he murmured. "What if our sun explodes without warning?"

I shrugged my shoulders.

"Show Biz," I commented.

He withdrew.

I had a feeling that he was hurrying home to pack his bags.

I had wanted to say to him, "Anyway, you couldn't sleep nights, you said, because you had heard that the *universe* was running down. The sun and the planets, however, are not the entire universe."

Yet, I am sure that he then would have said, "Okay, what about the rest of it? Is everything expected to explode, disintegrate, or simply run down . . . ?"

I would, admittedly, have been somewhat uneasy right there. For the correct answer very probably is, "Yes. The universe seems to be running down."

Yet, I had better hasten to add that I don't know what *the universe* is. The more valid term to use is "the known universe." We can see only so far with our telescopes, to a distance of some billions of light years (one light year is about 6,000,000,000,000 miles, the distance light travels in one year). With our radio telescopes we can "hear" farther. Yet, we still cannot pick up radio waves from the farthest reaches of the universe, if that means anything.

Well, then, is the known universe running down?

Apparently, it is.

Now what do I mean, exactly? It's something like this: the hot stars radiate their energy, and consequently they have to wear out, eventually; either they simply burn themselves out slowly, or they explode. The result is the same. They've had it.

Meanwhile, the cooler objects—such as the earth, other planets, and gases in space—warm up somewhat by absorbing the radiated energy of the waning stars, or suns. And there you have it. Finally, everything is at the same temperature, and the universe runs down. Then, no more energy exchanges can occur; everything is blah. Presumably, life ends.

Suppose we mix hot with cold water. We get lukewarm water. In a way, the same thing happens when a star radiates. The earth, other planets, and gaseous clouds, as we have noted, absorb the released radiant energy. But things are neither hot nor cold. Everything, as we have observed, is finally at the same temperature. It is lukewarm.

We can point to an everyday example of this apparent tendency of things around us to achieve a lukewarmness. If we burn fuel in our car, we are using up highly concentrated energy. The car moves, the exhaust gases mix with the whole atmosphere, and, finally, what is the result? The car is at another place, but the highly organized, high-level energy of the gasoline exists no more. We have added to the world's *unavailable energy*. We have brought high-level energy to a lower grade. We have increased the amount of degraded energy.

Natural processes certainly seem to function in this manner. Rocks tumble down a hill instead of up. We get noise from the rock, and it's gone. The sound energy dissipates into the atmosphere. The rock is at the bottom of the hill, and it won't roll up again, by itself. A forest fire consumes trees, a highly organized fuel. The heat spreads throughout the atmosphere—and that's that. No more trees.

Now I'm not saying that energy as a whole is lost. The atmosphere does warm up somewhat, doesn't it? I am saying that the energy is degraded, dissipated, spread thin. And we can't use it again, if we leave it alone. The warmth of the atmosphere never again becomes a forest fire. The fire never turns back into trees and oxygen.

Of course, if we want to get into the act, and exert ourselves, we could at least put the rock back up on the cliff.

Yes, but was that movement free? We used up the highly organized energy of our bodies—our calories—to do the job. And these calories are gone. The body is at a lower level, and we are part of the universe.

Moreover, in lifting the rock, we also waste some of our energy in friction against the atmosphere as we lug our burden, and in friction against the ground as our feet scramble about. We also waste energy in exhaling warmth and in panting as we fight the running down of the universe.

In the nineteenth century, certain German philosophers and theoretical scientists accepted unquestionably this theory that the universe is running down. They foresaw a gloomy outcome. In the end, they reasoned, the universe would succumb to *Wärme Tod,* or Heat Death.

At Heat Death, we would have no more motion, no exchanges of energy, and no more life. All life and all activity, these German scientists knew, requires that some regions (or bodies) have highly organized energy to react with their surroundings. In effect, differences of temperature must exist for anything at all to happen. Existing concentrated fuels or energies must generate temperatures higher than the surroundings.

An eventual total *Wärme Tod* certainly seemed as if it would be the end of the line. And, certainly, it all seemed irreversible. The sound which the rock made rumbling down the cliff does not extricate itself from the atmosphere, nor

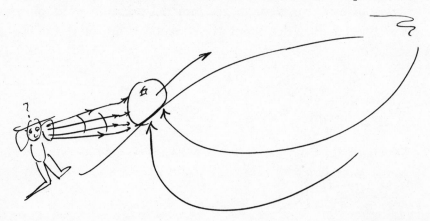

from our ears. Lukewarm water never separates itself into hot and cold portions. The universe, in brief, never runs backwards, as can a motion picture.

Do we, in actuality to this day, believe in this idea? Is *Wärme Tod* our fate? No, we no longer believe it. At least, most physicists don't go for a final, total, "everlasting" *Wärme Tod*. Why not?

We now, for instance, really believe in the existence of atoms and molecules and we now comprehend what this knowledge implies. Let's start with a bucket of lukewarm water.

The lukewarm water is not at all a static substance. Its *average* effect, yes, is that of a lukewarm condition. But in reality it consists of *fast* molecules, slow molecules, and molecules having near-average speeds. All these molecules are in constant motion, colliding with each other and with the walls of the container, gaining speeds, losing speeds, exchanging speeds.

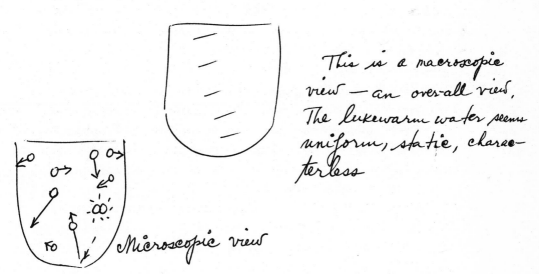

This is a macroscopic view — an over-all view. The lukewarm water seems uniform, static, characterless

Microscopic view

So what? So it means that a chance exists that by random motions, some day, a significant fraction of all the molecules will gather at the *left,* and a large number of slow ones will gather at the *right.* Then what? Then the left side of the bucket will be *hot,* and the right side will be *cold.* The water in the bucket is no longer lukewarm.

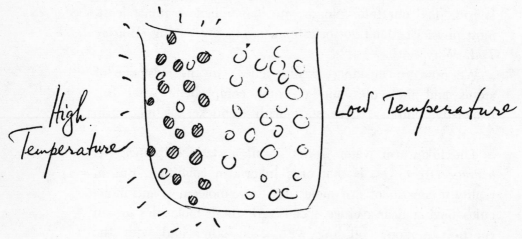

And in that case, we are back where we started, essentially: the hot side can begin to mix with the cold side, and the world of the bucket is at the beginning of its time. Mixing is about to begin.

Or, let's think of a teakettle on the stove. What do we expect? The water will get hotter as the faster molecules of the flame communicate their energy to the aluminum bottom of the teakettle, which, in turn communicates the energy of its atoms to the slower molecules of the water. That is the expected situation, and can be rather depended upon or we'd be in trouble at tea-time.

Yet, is it not seemingly a question of chance? In other words, is it possible that, if we put enough teakettles on enough stoves, someday the faster molecules of the cold water will move *en masse* toward the bottom, and the flame will get hotter, while the water turns to ice? Do you deny this possibility?

Or, consider this possibility. A monkey sits at a typewriter and pecks away between bites on a banana. Is there any chance that after many hours there will appear the word "cat"? I think that could happen, don't you? And is there any chance that someday, if you keep the bananas going—and the paper—you'll see the words "I don't like a cat, but I'm nuts about bananas"? It may take years and years of effort, and it may now be the monkey's grandson working at a new typewriter, but do you think it could happen?

If you do, then what about the supposition of the great physicist Professor Edington, that, if you wait long enough, someday the monkey (and his descendants) will have typed, without a single mistake, every book in one of the largest libraries in London? Do you think this could happen?

Or, let me ask this: If we toss one million pennies into the air, could they possibly come up heads, everyone of them? We'll let you toss them any number of times that you want.

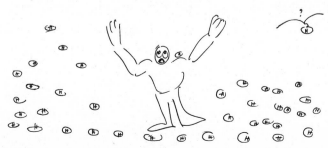

The point is, of course, that the microscopic nature of matter, with the existence of atoms, and their random motions, makes the "impossible" *possible*. There is even the probability, however small, that the universe after it runs down, with stars cooling and planets warming en route to Heat Death, may start to "run up" or tune up again. We would then have the somewhat rare event of the faster molecules segregating themselves out in space, flowing toward a region where they produce a *hot* star. The lukewarm planets would cool off, as their hot molecules leave. We would then have a local cycle ready to begin again, as though time had reversed itself.

There is a story about two physics students, one of whom tells his friend all about these matters, and winds up by saying, "Bill, the whole universe will begin all over again, and possibly in *exactly the same way*. And so, someday, you and I will be here again. Could you lend me five bucks, and when we meet in the new cycle, I'll pay you back?"

The other one replies, "This *is* the other cycle. And you borrowed the money the last time. Now pay me back."

Admittedly, the tendency of natural events is such that *order decreases*. A hot star, for example, represents a condition of *order*: all of the molecules are hot and they all are together in one spot. This condition, however, deteriorates and *disorder* increases. That is, *mixing* tends to take place. Highly concentrated energies fall apart and spread thinly throughout the universe. We say that the unavailable energy of the universe tends to increase.

A measure of this unavailable energy is called "entropy." Lord Kelvin put the idea this way:

> It is impossible by any means of any continuous inanimate agency to derive mechanical work from any portion of matter by cooling it below the lowest temperature of its surroundings.

We say, nowadays, "The entropy of the universe tends toward a maximum." That is, the universe tends to reach the state of complete mixing, or the condition of utter lukewarmness. We also often say, "Heat runs from hot bodies to the colder ones", and not the reverse. Yet, this is not the absolute law, as we have seen by considering all of those peculiar cases, which are based on an atomic structure of everything in the universe.

The physicist Clausius enunciated the general tendency this way, "It is impossible for a self-acting machine to convey heat continuously from one body to another at a higher temperature."

Of course, in a refrigerator, heat goes from the *cold* food to the hot machine. Yet, this is not a self-acting machine. It is operated by the external energy supplied by electricity.

Clausius implied that if we merely leave hot and cold bodies alone, the hotter will cool, and the cooler will warm up.

How about the vast oceans! Why don't we take the low-grade heat of the oceans, concentrate it, then use it to operate the works of man?

The oceans in general are colder than the surroundings, and their low-grade heat will not flow "up hill" toward substances already higher in temperature. Heat goes the other way, from hot to cold.

Of course, if we use energy to work on the water, we can extract their heat as they turn to ice. But the extraction will *cost* us energy. In fact, we will create more unavailable energy than we get by our machinations. We will increase the entropy of the universe. We will be taken further down the line leading to the Wärme Tod.

Yet, as we have seen, the microscopic view forces us to modify these statements. We must say that, left to itself, the universe is such that changes toward higher concentrations of energy *can* occur, though they are not likely to occur. We must even say that *large* changes in the "wrong direction" can occur, although they are very unlikely.

What do you think of this statement:

"Small changes toward *less* entropy, (or *more order*) can occur. And such small changes toward less entropy are more likely than *large* changes toward *less* entropy."

I have introduced some jargon, here, but are we not merely repeating what we have previously considered?

What is the outcome of all this? The outcome is a happy one. The universe may run down, yet I expect it to run up again.

Lord Kelvin—whose original name was William Thomson —was very much interested in such subjects all of his life, and he considerably advanced our knowledge of the workings of the universe. William, who as a boy enjoyed working on scientific puzzles with his brother James, was born in Belfast, Ireland, where his father was a mathematics teacher. When William was eight years old, the family moved to Glasgow, where the father became a Professor of Mathematics at the University.

William eventually studied at Cambridge, England, and in Paris. He himself became a Professor of Natural Philosophy at the University of Glasgow, at the age of twenty-two. And, believe it or not, he remained at this post for fifty-three years.

William was interested in the heat of the earth. He assumed that the earth had been very hot once upon a time, and that since its early days it had been cooling (entropy of the universe increasing; heat flowing toward cold). William then studied mathematically how a solid sphere should cool, and he estimated how long it would take for the surface of the sphere to reach the temperature that earth has today.

He calculated that the earth *began* as a hot sphere at most some 400 million years ago. Yet this figure is not right. There were facts about the earth he could not have known until the scientists Henri Becquerel (1852-1908) and Marie Curie (1867-1934) later made their startling discoveries.

They found that new heat keeps coming into existence from the radioactive substances inside the earth!

But, William Thomson concluded the surface of the earth is relatively hot because it has not had time to cool off very much. Today, we believe the earth is perhaps some five billion years old.

William Thomson, in his study and research, worked out a brilliant effect with a gifted amateur scientist named James Prescott Joule.

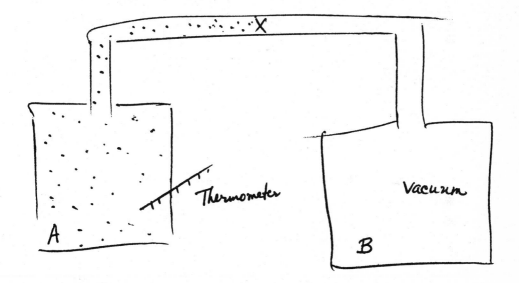

Let us start with two inter-connecting chambers, one having gas in it, say air, and the other one pumped out. Now we open the valve. What happens? Some of the gas, of course, spreads into B. Yet the exciting happening is this: the *temperature of the gas falls.*

This is called the Joule-Thomson Effect. But what is the explanation? It goes like this:

When the atoms were all in *A*, they were moving, on the average, at speeds V_1, and any two atoms were a distance, say *d*, apart. When they spread out, the average distance between any two atoms is of course greater than when they are close together. So what? The atoms, which attract each other, have in effect been *pulled away* from each other, as though springs between them had been stretched. Thus, their "spring energy," or potential energy, has increased. It is somewhat similar to lifting rocks up onto a higher cliff: if they ever come down, we'll get plenty of energy displayed. The atoms, if they ever draw toward each other, also will move faster and faster, and will display their energy.

We have, then, an increase in the potential energy of the atoms.

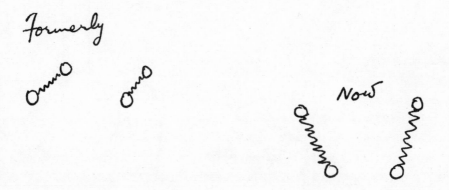

Yet, no energy has been given to the system. And, if one kind of energy has increased, another kind must have paid for it. The increase in potential energy has come from the *motions* of the atoms. The atoms must be now moving more slowly than before! They have given away some of their kinetic energy. Accordingly, if the atoms of a gas begin to move more slowly, the thermometer will be struck less violently. That is, the temperature will drop.

It is an astonishing conception. And it is the basis of the principle of the refrigerator—the Kelvinator! If a gas expands, it cools. The cooled gas steals heat from the food. The food cools. If it weren't for the work of Kelvin and Joule, a certain attractive woman on television would not at one time have had a fine job opening refrigerator doors. I wonder if she ever thanks her original sponsors?

Cooling by expansion has an effect on our weather. For example, when air rises over a mountain, it expands, because the pressure of the atmosphere is less at the heights than in the valley. The air expands and thereby cools so much that droplets form. Rain begins to fall. Going down hill, the atmosphere compresses the air. The air rolls away dry and hot.

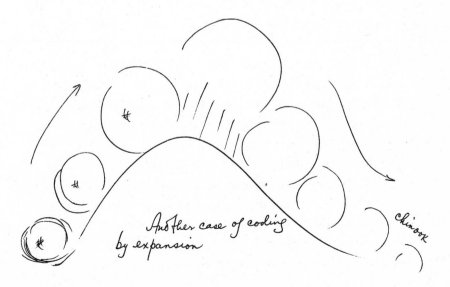

William Thomson, or Lord Kelvin, accomplished a great deal more than inventing the refrigerator. He calculated that there must be a *lowest* temperature in the universe. At such a temperature, the atoms would stop moving completely, and go to sleep.

How could there be a temperature lower than the one at which the atoms do not move at all? Possibly, there are yet one or two refinements. Perhaps we can extract heat from some of the smaller parts of the atoms. We can. We are able to extract heat from the *nuclei* of the atoms by forcing them into a lower energy condition.

The lowest possible temperature is about −273° C. Believe it or not, we have been able to achieve almost this absolute zero of temperature. We have gone to within about .000001° C. of absolute zero! Brother, that is cold.

Would it make any sense to speak of −274° C., or −300° C.? No, not if we go along with the atomic notions. Not if we accept the theories concerning moving particles and how their speeds correspond to temperature.

We like to speak of temperature as beginning at Kelvin's Absolute Zero. Doesn't that make good sense? So we have a Kelvin Scale.

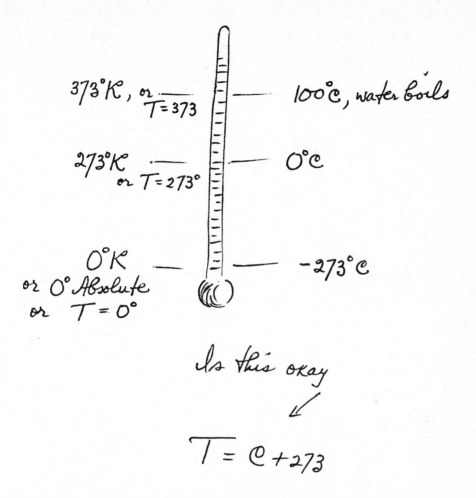

$373°K$, or $\dfrac{}{T=373}$ $100°C$, water boils

$273°K$ or $T=273°$ $0°C$

$0°K$ or $0°$ Absolute or $T=0°$ $-273°C$

Is this okay

$$T = C + 273$$

Lord Kelvin worked out this absolute scale and the absolute zero through the ideas of heat flowing toward cold, such as we have previously considered. We can think of a machine that has energy given to it—let's say in the form of heat. The machine works. Perhaps it pushes something. Then there is the *exhaust* heat. If only the exhaust could be at *absolute zero!* Boy, would we have an efficient machine!

To get an exhaust of absolute zero, we would have to squeeze everything out of the working fuel. We would have to extract all the energy. All that would be left would be an absolutely blah exhaust. A really exhausted exhaust.

Kelvin's engine has this formula, where E is the efficiency, T_1 is the absolute temperature of the intake heat, and T_2 is the temperature of the exhaust heat:

$$E = \frac{T_1 - T_2}{T_1} \times 100$$

You can think of such a formula as giving a definition of absolute temperature.

By the way, all this reminds me to put down three important laws, which describe in a very sweeping way how the universe operates, as far as energy, matter, and temperature are concerned.

1. Energy *plus* mass remains unchanged in any enclosed system.

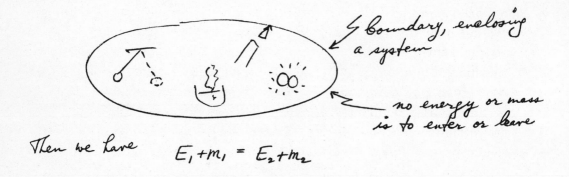

This clearly means that within any bounded region, such as a completely isolated and insulated room, or even the known universe itself, if energy decreases, then mass increases, and vice versa.

In Kelvin's time, we used to say, "Energy is conserved in a closed system, although it may change form." And, "Matter is conserved in a closed system, although it may change form."

But Einstein's work has changed this to: Energy *plus* mass in a closed system is conserved, though they may change form or they may change into each other.

Remember $E = mc^2$? E is the energy which *appears* when an amount of mass m vanishes. And we know that c is the speed of light.

Actually, Einstein's $E = mc^2$ came out in 1905, and Kelvin lived until 1907. Thus, he knew that the world was changing, though I must say that he was somewhat surprised.

The next sweeping law is:

2. The unavailable energy of the universe tends toward a maximum. Or, heat flows toward cold. Yet, remember! This does not occur in every single instance, but only *on the whole*. Do you recall how Kelvin expressed this law?

The third law deals with the absolute zero:

3. There *is* a lowest temperature, and bodies at this temperature have no more energy to give us.

What a magnificent comprehension these three *laws of thermodynamics* give us. It is thrilling to understand how the laws are used for atoms and solar systems, and for galaxies and the known universe.

William Thomson gave us more than we have a right to expect from one man—and we haven't even touched upon his numerous inventions, his theory of batteries, and the trans-Atlantic cable. He published more than three hundred original papers. Think what this means. It is hard to believe.

Through his life he was known for his modesty, even shyness, and he was recognized as one of the kindest of men, a man devoted to his assistants and to his students. This man received an avalanche of honors, among them the title of Baron Kelvin of Largs, or Lord Kelvin. A statue of Lord Kelvin was put up in Glasgow after his death.

Yet, his statue is in his work, as every scientist knows.

Mendeleyev

THE BETTMANN ARCHIVE

16

Dmitri Mendeleyev

1834-1907

On August 7, 1887, the great Russian chemist Mendeleyev went up in a balloon *alone,* to study a solar eclipse. He was supposed to have been taken up by an aeronaut, but at the very last moment it was discovered that the balloon could lift only one man. So, Mendeleyev, who knew nothing about the controls, said, "I'm going alone—good bye, everybody."

He made it. And returned safely.

Do you consider Mendeleyev exceptionally brave for having made the balloon flight? I do. Let me tell you, however, of an accomplishment even bolder achieved by him a number of years before the balloon adventure.

For years he had been seeking a plan of unity among the chemical elements, and even among their compounds.

He was taking nothing for granted. He performed thousands of experiments with his own hands. He made thousands of calculations, wrote innumerable letters, and studied countless reports. Everything in the world that was known about the chemical elements Mendeleyev seemed to know! Throughout months, throughout years, he searched for missing data, which he then checked himself.

In hundreds of laboratories throughout the world, thousands of chemists had labored for years on copper, silver, gold, sodium, lithium, potassium. Mendeleyev knew the results of their work. In French, Spanish, Italian, German, and English he perused their reports and followed their continuing labors. The brain in his great blond head absorbed the information and sifted it.

One day, in 1869, his niece, Nadezhda, came to see him.

"I promised to explain to you my periodic system of the elements," he said, and walked over to the far wall.

Nadezhda followed him and stood open-mouthed before the rows and columns of white cards on the wall.

"How strange," she murmured. "How important. How awfully, awfully important."

He pointed at the cards with his long forefinger.

"Every element in the world is made up of tiny particles which we call 'atoms'. There are now known about sixty different kinds of elements, so there are about sixty different atoms. Each kind of atom weighs a certain amount."

Nadezhda drew closer and read the names on the cards.

"These are the elements," Mendeleyev explained. "They are arranged according to the weights of their atoms. You could have just simply one long vertical column from lightest to heaviest. When you do that then the following is known to be true:

The first one that I have here, lithium, resembles the eighth one, sodium. And the second one, beryllium, resembles the ninth one, magnesium. Thus it goes, essentially, with certain refinements. So you see, after a lapse of seven we get an element of similar characteristics again. This lapse or interval I call a period. This is a periodic system. After a certain lapse or period in counting, we get again an element similar to one way above. In this way we get entire groups which resemble each other. . . ."

Nadezhda pointed to the cards.

"But how do they resemble each other?" she asked. "Do they look alike?"

"In many ways," he said. "Chemically, for example. Take the first group. Every element there, lithium, sodium, potassium, and so on, behaves like this: two atoms of lithium will combine with one atom of oxygen. And two atoms of sodium also will combine with one atom of oxygen. And the same is true for potassium, and so on. On the other hand, in another group which I get by that periodic selection, one atom of each element wants to combine with one atom of oxygen, to form an oxygen compound, of course. This is true for the group with beryllium, calcium, strontium, and so on. Then another group contains elements for which each atom wants to combine with three atoms of oxygen—if given a chance . . . "

"How clever!" said Nadezhda. "How simply clever of them."

Mendeleyev coughed.

"Well," he said. "Some day I will explain some more."

November 1870 came and Mendeleyev was putting his plan into final form. Certain changes had to be made if the scheme was to be consistent. Boldly, he changed the

213

atomic weights of a number of elements, since, as they stood, they did not fit in with his plan. Gold, with a quoted weight of 196.2 should have been placed *before* such elements as platinum, iridium, and osmium, of atomic weights 196.7, 197, 198.6. But Mendeleyev, feeling that their weights were wrong, put gold after these elements. He proved to be right, and at his time the order was osmium, 190.2; iridium, 193.1; platinum, 195.2; and gold, 197.2. He made other changes, too, among them uranium, from 120 to 240.

"The laws of nature admit of no exception," he wrote, "and in this they clearly differ from such rules and maxims as are found in grammar, and in other inventions, methods, and relations of man's creation.

"It is necessary to do one thing or the other—either to consider the periodic law as completely true, and as forming a new instrument in chemical research, or to refute it."

Mendeleyev was working incessantly on his plan. As fast as he could tear himself from his lectures, he rushed, as though in a trance, to the private study of his university apartment.

There was no time for anything else now. There was hardly time for food. He no longer came to the table to eat. With nervous energy, the tall shaggy Mendeleyev, head and hands in quick movement, concentrated upon his problem. Stooped and gaunt from late work during the nights, he strode about his study, pen in hand, now stopping to gaze upon the array of white cards pinned upon the wall across from his desk, now dropping down onto the yellow sofa to jot down an elusive idea.

"A look at the table of the elements reveals a number of empty places.

"I am now going to make such predictions of the existence of certain elements as yet unknown in order to make a test of my system.

"In the row of more or less ordinary elements there seem lacking analogues of boron or aluminium, as a glance at the table shows. In the third group there is an element lacking right after aluminium. From studying the table, and from considering the nature of the elements which surround this blank space I conclude that the weights of the atoms of this undiscovered element is about 45. This can be seen by interpolating between the values of calcium, 40, and of titanium, 48. As is obvious, two atoms of this unknown, X, will combine with three atoms of oxygen to form the oxide X_2O_3. . . . The unknown will combine with sodium, lithium, and so on, and will not be dissolved by water. With acids this unknown will form permanent salts. . . . In any case, ammonia will not dissolve it. . . . I propose to call this undiscovered element 'ekaboron.' The prefix 'eka' means 'one' in Sanskrit, and here it is used to indicate 'resemblance to.' Thus ekaboron, or Eb 45.

"Eb will be metallic in appearance. And the weight of 1 cubic centimeter of Eb will be 3 grams. It will not be volatile, and therefore it is not likely to be found by the spectroscopic method where it is necessary to have the substance glowing as a vapor to emit its characteristic colors. Ekaboron will not break up water into hydrogen and oxygen at ordinary temperatures, but at somewhat higher temperatures it will do so.

"Of course Eb will dissolve in acids.

"One atom of Eb will combine with three atoms of chlorine to produce $EbCl_3$ (possibly two atoms of Eb will prefer six of chlorine, Eb_2Cl_6). This chloride must be volatile. . . . The weight of 1 cubic centimeter of the chloride will be 2 grams. Ekaboron will offer two atoms against three, of course, in forming a combination with oxygen, Eb_2O_3. This must be nonvolatile, and not soluble in water. . . .

"I shall now predict the nature of another undiscovered element, also in group 3; in fact an element right below ekaboron. To this one I shall give the temporary name of 'eka-aluminium.' The weight of its atoms will be 68. Its salts will be more stable than those of aluminium. . . . The weight of 1 cubic centimeter in the metallic state will be about 6. Eka-aluminium will be more volatile than aluminium, and a spectroscopic discovery is possible."

Mendeleyev then made a brief prediction as to a few more elements.

"But now I wish to take up a most interesting one. This one I will call 'ekasilicon.' It is at present a blank space in the fourth group. We may write this element as 'Es', and the weight of its atoms should be 72. The oxide of course is EsO_2. The weight of 1 cubic centimeter of free ekasilicon will be about 5.5 grams. It will be a fusible metal, capable of vaporizing in strong heat. . . . The weight of 1 cubic centimeter of EsO_2 will be about 4.7 grams. The chloride $EsCl_4$, must be soluble in water. The weight of 1 cubic centimeter of it will be about 1.9 grams. Ekasilicon will form the compound EsH_4 with hydrogen. . . ."

Other men had thought about a unity among the elements. Others had made schemes and plans tending to show relations among the fundamental substances of the universe, that is, among the known elements.

In France, there had been De Chancourtois; in Germany, Lothar Meyer, in England, Newlands. None had dared challenge the then accepted figures for the atomic weights of the elements, or change these figures to obtain a more logical scheme of unity. None had dreamed of prophesying the existence of undiscovered elements, or of giving their attributes in minute mathematical detail.

But Mendeleyev had done it.

His report containing the prophecies appeared in the *Journal of the Russian Chemical Society,* in the issue of January 7, 1871.

When the details of the predictions became known, chemists and physicists looked at each other and silently wondered. What was there in the character of a man, who, having a successful career in science, suddenly risks his reputation in so bold and perhaps unnecessary a way?

In Russia they wondered about Mendeleyev. Abroad, the few who bothered to think of the work of a Russian shrugged their shoulders.

Then, in 1875 it happened. One of the elements was found.

The discovery had been made by the French chemist Lecoq de Boisbaudran.

De Boisbaudran had done much work in spectrum analysis. One day, while flaming a zinc blende from the Pyrenees, he observed a brilliant violet line in the spectroscope. This color fell at the place marked 417. The length of these violet waves of light was thus 417 millionths of a millimeter. De Boisbaudran knew that this was a new line. The French scientist, believing that he had found a new element, began the investigation of the substance hidden within the zinc blende.

He separated out something and recognized its difference from zinc, and from cadmium and indium, as well as the other companions of zinc. This, too, he did by the spectroscope, matching and comparing the various glowing lines. Then de Boisbaudran began to perform chemical tests on the new substance. He determined as many properties as he could. It was difficult work, for he had been able to extract only a very small amount of the new element as yet. He tried to determine the atomic weight, the weight of 1 cubic centimeter of the material, the boiling point, reactions with other substances.

De Boisbaudran and two of his colleagues remembered something. They got out a Russian journal of 1871, and turned the pages. With a Russian-French dictionary the three Frenchmen went to work on the article by D. Mendeleyev. Late at night they sat staring at two columns on a sheet of paper. In one column they had listed the already determined properties of de Boisbaudran's new element. In a parallel column they had just finished listing the properties of the predicted eka-aluminium. The Frenchmen stared. The match was very close.

"Mon Dieu!" said one. "Mon Dieu! But he is some fellow, this Russian!"

His colleague reached into a glass cabinet and produced a bottle of champagne. He poured three bubbling glasses.

"To this Russian," he said. "To this Mendeleyev."

Lecoq de Boisbaudran named the new element "gallium" in honor of the ancient name of his country. But it was Mendeleyev's "eka-aluminium."

Mendeleyev sat down and wrote out more properties to be expected from the element eka-aluminium, or gallium. These, too, were confirmed. Now there was no question that it was in fact the predicted eka-aluminium.

The Frenchmen poured more champagne.

"To this Mendeleyev," they said. "A man!"

Now almost the entire world of science read Mendeleyev's old article. He had predicted other elements. The shoulders now did not shrug.

At Princeton University, a gray-haired man sat staring at a scientific report.

"Mendeleyev," he said. "I wonder how he pronounces that. Mendeleyev. So it has been found. Well, well, well."

He turned in his chair and spoke to a young woman at a desk.

"Miss Jackson," he said. "You better fill out an order card for that Russian magazine mentioned in this footnote."

The young woman stared.

"Russian?" she demanded. "You mean Russian?"

The gray-haired man gave a look of hopelessness.

"Yes," he said. "I'm afraid so. One has to keep up in one's field."

Then it happened again. In 1879. And in 1886. In Freiburg, the chemist Clemens Winkler found a new element.

Winkler had set out to follow the clue given by the Russian Mendeleyev in his predictions of 1871. The Russian had actually suggested where to seek for an element which he named "ekasilicon." The German scientist was seeking a grayish element whose atoms would be about seventy-two times as heavy as those of hydrogen.

According to Mendeleyev's prediction, the weight of the new element was expected to be about 5.5 times that of water—that is, 1 cubic centimeter of it should weigh 5.5 grams. There were of course a great many other properties predicted. The element, for example, would be slightly susceptible to acids.

Winkler examined the silver ore argyrodite and extracted a grayish substance. Its atomic weight was 72.3 and 1 cubic centimeter of it weighed 5.5 grams. When Winkler made the substance combine with oxygen he found that the resultant oxide weighed exactly what Mendeleyev had predicted. Then Winkler made an ethide and found that it would boil at Mendeleyev's predicted temperature. Winkler made other tests, and finally he flamed the new substance and looked through the spectroscope. The set of bright colored lines was new. No known substance could emit this particular set of colors. This was a new element.

Winkler wrote, "There is no doubt that this is Mendeleyev's 'ekasilicon.' The correspondence is remarkable. Even amazing." He named the new element "germanium."

When the news reached Russia, people in the universities and students in the high schools felt a thrill of pride. The news also reached England, France, Holland, Italy, and America. And in these lands, too, both scientists and laymen stopped a moment to marvel as they had before. In England, the commotion in scientific circles was inordinate. Three elements that the outlandish, hairy foreigner had predicted in detail, had been found—eka-aluminium in 1875 by Lecoq de Boisbaudran, and named "gallium"; ekaboron in 1879 by

L. F. Nilson, and named "scandium"; and now in 1886 eka-silicon by Clemens Winkler, and named "germanium."

In 1846, the existence of the planet Neptune had been predicted accurately. This Mendeleyev, however, had in great detail predicted the three terrestrial "planets" which had now been found.

Scientists marveled even more when the final tables of comparison between Mendeleyev's ekasilicon and the newly named germanium became known:

PROPERTY	EKASILICON (Es)	GERMANIUM (Ge)
1. Weight of atoms (compared to hydrogen)	72	72.3
2. Weight of 1 cubic centimeter (compared to water)	5.5	5.469
3. Heat required to warm the 1 cubic centimeter by 1° C. (compared to water)	0.073	0.076
4. One atom will combine with 2 atoms of chlorine to form	$EsCl_4$	$GeCl_4$
5. Weight of 1 cubic centimeter of the oxygen compound (compared to water)	4.7	4.703
6. One atom will combine with 4 atoms of chlorine to form	$EsCl_4$	$GeCl_4$
7. The compound with chlorine will melt at about	90° C.	86° C.
8. The weight of 1 cubic centimeter of the chlorine compound (compared to water) will be	1.9	1.887
9. The ethide compound will exist	$Es(C_2H_5)_4$	$Ge(C_2H_5)_4$
10. The above compound will melt at	160°	160°
11. The weight of 1 cubic centimeter of the above compound (relative to water) will be	0.96	1.0

So the elements that Mendeleyev predicted were discovered. There was gallium, discovered by de Boisbaudran, in 1875; there was scandium, found by Nilson in 1879; there was germanium, discovered by Winkler in 1886. . . .

Yet, all this was only a small part of all that Mendeleyev did in chemistry. He published hundreds of articles on his researches, and many books. In general, he tackled a mass of seemingly unrelated chemical formulas, equations, brews and concoctions, and from them made the *science* of chemistry.

I like to reflect on some of his comments about science and about the world:

It is the function of science to discover the existence of a general reign of order in nature and to find the causes governing this order. And this refers in equal measure to the relations of man—social and political—and to the entire universe as a whole.

There exists everywhere a medium in things, determined by equilibrium. The Russian proverb says, "Too much salt or too little salt is alike an evil." It is the same in political and social relations.

Knowing how contented, joyous, and free is life in the realm of science, one fervently wishes that many would enter its portals.

And one who entered these portals was a young man who improved upon Mendeleyev's plan of unity for the elements.

His name was Henry Gwyn-Jeffreys Moseley.

Meanwhile, through the long years in Russia, some peasant mothers tell their children of a great bearded man who flew to heaven on a bubble.

And when a child asks, "Where is he now? What is he doing?" the mother replies, "They say, little dove, that he is in heaven, talking to God, telling him of our sorrows."

Moseley

Henry Moseley

1887-1915

On August 10, 1915, a bullet was fired into the British troops at Gallipoli. The British had come to storm their way against the resisting Turks, who were allies of the Germans. The British wanted to force their way from the Mediterranean into the Black Sea, but the Turks and their German friends were giving them a bad time by cannonading from the hills.

Here were the romantic Straits of the Dardanelles—the "Hellespont" of Hero and Leander. Leander had been able to swim the Hellespont! And Byron matched the feat. It was quite a swim—one mile. But ships of war, passing through the channel, find it a narrow bottleneck. For the warships, this is no long, romantic, and challenging swim.

The British had begun their attempt to force the Straits in February of 1915, to help the Russians against the Central Powers. A naval attack launched on March 18 failed. After that, the wily German Marshal Liman von Sanders made sweeping changes and brought in re-enforcements to devise an even better defense for his Turkish allies.

The British began to accumulate larger forces of their own, preparatory to a landing. They were assembling five divisions—two of them the 29th and the Royal Naval, two made of Australians and New Zealanders, and the fifth a French Colonial division. By May, the British brought in the 42nd Division. In time, they added five additional divisions of their own to the invasion force.

On August 6, the grand offensive began against the Turks and Germans at Gallipoli.

The British and their friends took a beating. The losses in ships and men were staggering.

Moreover, a certain bullet had been fired at them. . . .

Henry Gwyn-Jeffreys Moseley, born in 1887, had been educated at Eton and Trinity College, Oxford. He had served as a Lecturer in Physics at Manchester University, and later he had taught at Oxford.

Scientific work had come easy to this shy young man, and he enjoyed his early investigations into radioactivity.

Moseley was well-liked. Some years ago, when I visited in England, I saw his office still preserved, with his portrait on a desk next to a chart of his remarkable work—a work that changed our entire understanding of the structure of an atom.

Mendeleyev, in devising his *Periodic Table of the Elements,* had made order out of chaos for chemistry. He had predicted the existence of certain elements, and they were, indeed, discovered.

Mendeleyev's basic conception was this: The weight of an atom determines whether it is an atom of hydrogen, or of gold, or of phosphorus. . . . The *weight* was the key. Atoms of different substances were different in weight. He had arranged his table according to the weights of the atoms, and thereby learned much and foresaw much.

Nevertheless, Henry Moseley, by the age of twenty-six, had showed that the world of the atom was something quite different from Mendeleyev's conception. Still, Moseley's achievements were based on Mendeleyev's work. He had to stand on the shoulders of the bearded, audacious Russian, who had preceded him in order to see further.

What did Moseley discover? He discovered that the amount of *electrical charge* residing within the heart of an atom determines the nature of that atom. The weight is of no basic consequence. If an atom has two positive charges in its nucleus, it is a helium atom; if it has eight positive charges, it is oxygen; if it has ninety-two, it is uranium.

In the Aetheneum, one of England's fine museums, I saw Moseley's original apparatus. It is a simple set of equipment, but it did its intended work.

Moseley's research went like this: He shot electrons at targets of various elements such as zinc, copper, gold . . . , and he studied the X rays which the targets emitted.

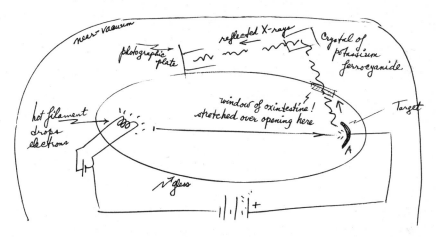

The X rays passed out of the glass container and were reflected by a crystal of potassium ferrocyanide onto a photographic plate. From the position of the image on the photographic plate, it was possible to determine the *wave length* of the X rays.

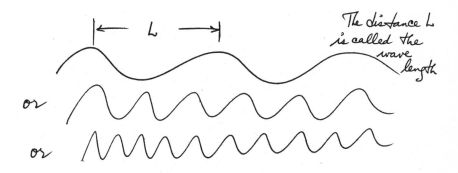

Moseley changed the target A (anode) without opening up the whole apparatus. They still have, at the Aetheneum, the little trolley that he used, by means of which various targets could come up to position A.

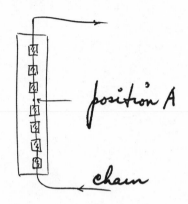

position A

chain

When a target rolled up to position A, it would make contact with the positive wire from the battery, and so would be ready to help accelerate electrons at itself. Thus, it would emit its X rays. The crystal, remember, is used simply to help bring sharp X ray images onto, the photographic plate by reflecting and focusing them.

Moseley found that the atoms of each element gave forth two separate sets of series of X rays.

Here is an example for *silver* (one Ångstrom is .00000001 cm):

about .000000004 cm in length, or .4×10^{-8} cm, or .4 Ångstroms or .4Å

Called K X-rays

These are short wave length, or high frequency

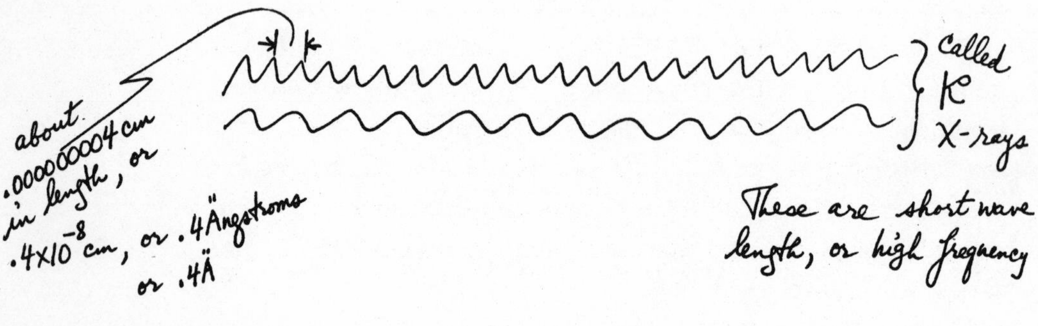

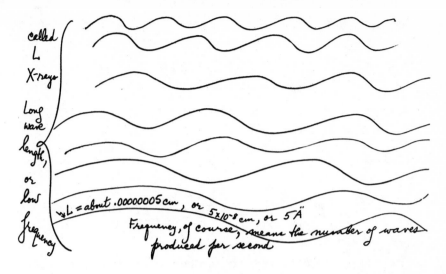

called
L
X-rays

Long
wave
length,

or
low

frequency

wL = about .00000005 cm, or 5×10⁻⁸ cm, or 5Å

Frequency, of course, means the number of waves produced per second

This method is too unwieldy a way of reporting the lengths of the waves. Hence, we simply make a graph like this:

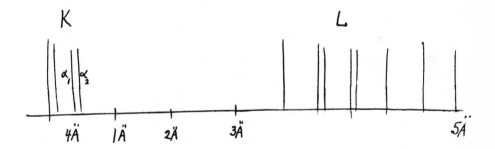

K

α_1 α_2

L

4Å   1Å   2Å   3Å   5Å

The various lines can be given names. For example, as shown above, we have α_1 and α_2.

As we have pointed out, for each element Moseley obtained patterns of the above form. Yet, the entire set of lines would be shifted with each element, either to the right or to the left. Here is what Moseley realized: the *character* of a given series is practically the same for all elements, but the wave length (and therefore the frequency) of a given line varies with each element.

When Moseley plotted only *one* line (say, $K\alpha_1$) for each

227

element against the atomic *weight,* he got this defective curve:

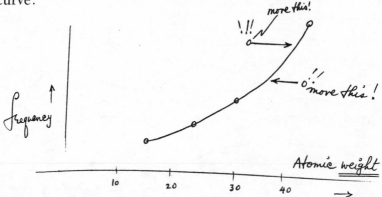

In order to get a smooth, progressive curve, one accommodating all points, Moseley had to invert nickel and cobalt in Mendeleyev's *Table of Elements,* even though a lighter atom would then follow a heavier one!

"Clearly," reasoned Moseley, "some other quality is more important than the weight of the atom."

So it was that Moseley began *numbering* the elements—1 for hydrogen, 2 for helium, 3 for lithium, 4 for beryllium, 5 for boron . . . with no regard whatever for the weights of their atoms, being guided only by the progressive increase of the frequency of the $K\alpha_1$ line.

As he plotted, Moseley found that his curve would be spoiled unless he left a gap at integer 43. Accordingly, he simply left a gap, and decided that an element was missing. Years later this element was found! We call it *technetium,* and it gives X rays that fit exactly on the curve.

(Incidentally, at this point, let me ask: Can you find four or five places in the modern periodic table where Moseley's numbers go breezily along despite the fact that an atom is lighter in weight than one which has immediately preceded it? I gave you one set: cobalt and nickel.)

Because of his work and that of other scientists on the nature of the atom, Moseley came to a certain conclusion

228

about the numbers which he had to assign to the elements in order to have a systematic change in the X ray lines. He maintained that each of these numbers stands for the amount of positive electrical charge in the heart, or nucleus, of the atom. These numbers are called "atomic numbers."

Let us take a look at how we now see the structure of the atom. Let us examine the three forms of hydrogen atoms:

First, *protium,* by far the most common hydrogen atom:

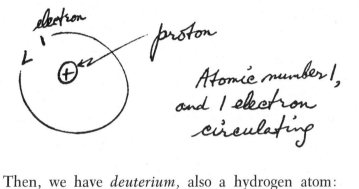

Then, we have *deuterium,* also a hydrogen atom:

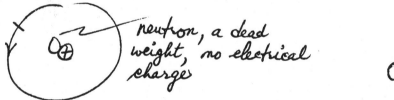

And *tritium,* which is very heavy hydrogen:

You can see clearly that the weight does not determine which chemical element we have. The *charge on the nucleus* is the determining factor.

Here is a helium atom:

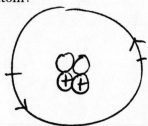

And this is a helium nucleus:

But this, too, is a helium atom. It is called "helium 3," or He^3:

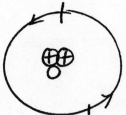

At the subscript position we can put the *atomic number*, or the number of protons in the nucleus. The superscript tells how many particles *all together* there are in the nucleus. Thus,

$$_2He^4, \ _2He^3, \ _1H^1, \ _1H^2, \ _1H^3$$

Let us look at uranium. There are a number of different uranium atoms:

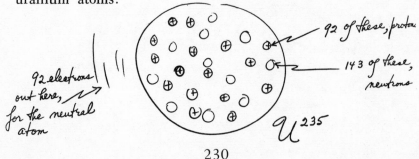

92 of these, protons

143 of these, neutrons

92 electrons out here, for the neutral atom

U^{235}

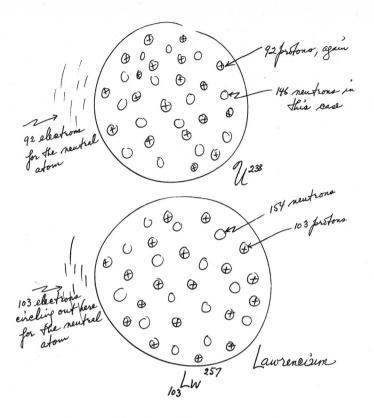

Of course, Henry Moseley did not know about neutrons, but he knew the essential point, the vital role of the positive charge in the heart of the atom.

Everyone knows, I suppose, that the various forms of one atom such as the hydrogen

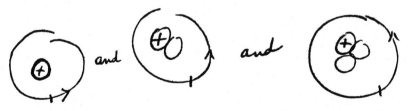

are called *isotopes*, which simply means "same type." (Can you guess in which language?)

There is one point that we have not yet taken up, and it is this:

How do the K and L series of X rays originate? Where do

they come from when energetic electrons go sailing into the atoms of some target?

Let us take an atom—lithium, for example, and use it as a target for an electron:

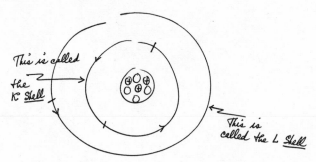

1. Here, now, is the sequence of events. A fast electron from the negative side within the X ray tube strikes a lithium atom—an atom within a lithium target on the positive side:

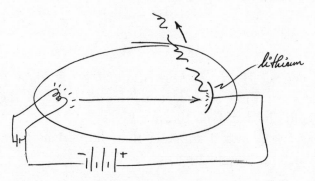

2. The electron (also called the "cathode ray") knocks one of the K electrons out of the atom:

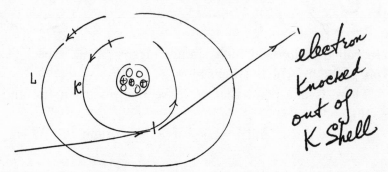

3. Now, an electron from the L shell drops to the K shell to fill the vacancy there. But! The L electrons have more energy than necessary to belong at K. So, the dropping L electron radiates a pulse of energy—a pulse of X rays! That's it!

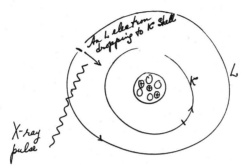

After that, the new K electron is well-behaved, quiet, and nonradiating, as it circles the nucleus.

The distribution of shells such as K and L depends upon the nuclear charge. And the energy radiated thus also depends upon the nuclear charge. So the nature of the X ray pulse in turn depends on the nuclear charge. Hence, the wave lengths of the X rays correspond to the magnitude of the atomic number, that is, the amount of positive nuclear charge.

All this is what Moseley determined. *He determined that each element can be given an atomic number corresponding to the wave length of the X rays which its atoms give off.* His discovery is one of the most beautiful developments in the history of science.

I should mention, too, that the larger atoms have more shells, to accommodate their larger supplies of external electrons. They have K, L, M, N, O, P, and Q shells. X rays, however, are given off only by electron jumps among the inner shells. Other jumps will give waves such as those of visible light.

PERIODIC TABLE OF THE ELEMENTS

Group Number

Period	Ia	IIa	IIIb	IVb	Vb	VIb	VIIb	VIII	VIII	VIII	Ib	IIb	IIIa	IVa	Va	VIa	VIIa	O
1	1 H 1.0080 Hydrogen																	2 He 4.003 Helium
2	3 Li 6.940 Lithium	4 Be 9.013 Beryllium											5 B 10.82 Boron	6 C 12.011 Carbon	7 N 14.008 Nitrogen	8 O 16.000 Oxygen	9 F 19.00 Fluorine	10 Ne 20.183 Neon
3	11 Na 22.991 Sodium	12 Mg 24.32 Magnesium											13 Al 26.98 Aluminum	14 Si 28.09 Silicon	15 P 30.975 Phosphorus	16 S 32.066 Sulfur	17 Cl 35.457 Chlorine	18 Ar 39.944 Argon
4	19 K 39.100 Potassium	20 Ca 40.08 Calcium	21 Sc 44.96 Scandium	22 Ti 47.90 Titanium	23 V 50.95 Vanadium	24 Cr 52.01 Chromium	25 Mn 54.94 Manganese	26 Fe 55.85 Iron	27 Co 58.94 Cobalt	28 Ni 58.71 Nickel	29 Cu 63.54 Copper	30 Zn 65.38 Zinc	31 Ga 69.72 Gallium	32 Ge 72.60 Germanium	33 As 74.91 Arsenic	34 Se 78.96 Selenium	35 Br 79.916 Bromine	36 Kr 83.80 Krypton
5	37 Rb 85.48 Rubidium	38 Sr 87.63 Strontium	39 Y 88.92 Yttrium	40 Zr 91.22 Zirconium	41 Nb 92.91 Niobium	42 Mo 95.95 Molybdenum	43 Tc (99) Technetium	44 Ru 101.1 Ruthenium	45 Rh 102.91 Rhodium	46 Pd 106.4 Palladium	47 Ag 107.880 Silver	48 Cd 112.41 Cadmium	49 In 114.82 Indium	50 Sn 118.70 Tin	51 Sb 121.76 Antimony	52 Te 127.61 Tellurium	53 I 126.91 Iodine	54 Xe 131.30 Xenon
6	55 Cs 132.91 Cesium	56 Ba 137.36 Barium	57 La 138.92 Lanthanum	72 Hf 178.50 Hafnium	73 Ta 180.95 Tantalum	74 W 183.86 Tungsten	75 Re 186.22 Rhenium	76 Os 190.2 Osmium	77 Ir 192.2 Iridium	78 Pt 195.09 Platinum	79 Au 197.0 Gold	80 Hg 200.61 Mercury	81 Tl 204.39 Thallium	82 Pb 207.21 Lead	83 Bi 209.00 Bismuth	84 Po (210) Polonium	85 At (210) Astatine	86 Rn (222) Radon
7	87 Fr (223) Francium	88 Ra 226.05 Radium	89 Ac 227.0 Actinium															

Lanthanide Series	58 Ce 140.13 Cerium	59 Pr 140.92 Praseodymium	60 Nd 144.27 Neodymium	61 Pm (145) Promethium	62 Sm 150.35 Samarium	63 Eu 152.0 Europium	64 Gd 157.26 Gadolinium	65 Tb 158.93 Terbium	66 Dy 162.51 Dysprosium	67 Ho 164.94 Holmium	68 Er 167.27 Erbium	69 Tm 168.94 Thulium	70 Yb 173.04 Ytterbium	71 Lu 174.99 Lutetium
Actinide Series	90 Th 232.05 Thorium	91 Pa (231) Protactinium	92 U 238.07 Uranium	93 Np (237) Neptunium	94 Pu (242) Plutonium	95 Am (243) Americium	96 Cm (247) Curium	97 Bk (249) Berkelium	98 Cf (251) Californium	99 Es (254) Einsteinium	100 Fm (253) Fermium	101 Md (256) Mendelevium	102 No (254) Nobelium	103 Lw (257) Lawrencium

A word should be said about those "shells." Each electron really has its own distinct orbit. We often draw the electrons as spaced along the same orbit merely to save time:

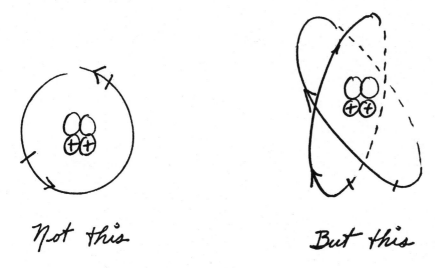

Not this   *But this*

Similarly, for lithium:

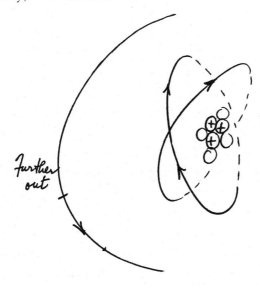

Further out

Perhaps you would like to study the *Periodic Table of the Elements* and explain what is "Periodic" about it.

235

Before I forget, I want to mention the fact that every atom has at least three important numbers associated with it. These three numbers are:

1. The *atomic number,* as we know, is the number of protons in the nucleus.

2. The *mass number* is the total number of protons and neutrons in the nucleus.

3. The *atomic weight* is simply the weight of the atom. (It doesn't matter much whether we mean the whole atom or the nucleus here, since the electrons weigh so little. A proton weighs about 1836 times as much as an electron.)

As an example of all three numbers, consider: $_2He^4$.

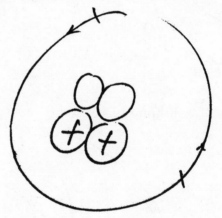

1. The atomic number is 2 (as determined by Moseley's method).

2. The mass number is 4, or 2 protons and 2 neutrons.

3. The atomic weight is 4.003 (compared with the oxygen atom taken as 16).

I spoke about Moseley to Professor J. S. Townsend once. Moseley was Townsend's protege in the early days of his development. I said, "Did he have to go to Gallipoli? What happened? Was he eager for combat?"

Professor Townsend replied, quietly, "No. He was a quiet fellow. A shy one, who just wanted to do his scientific work.

And about the war—he seemed to think that he ought to go."

A bullet was fired at Gallipoli.

The bullet sped through the air. It entered the brain of one of the greatest geniuses England ever produced, a young man, aged twenty-eight.

Henry Gwyn-Jeffreys Moseley, shy, studious, inspired, was killed in one of our wars.

They have built gross outward statues to Caesars and Napoleons. The statues for Henry Moseley are secure in the inner hearts of the atoms.

Röntgen

18

Wilhelm Konrad Röntgen

1845-1923

There is a way of looking inside an oyster without opening it—in case you are looking for pearls. Incidentally, to an oyster, a pearl is simply a lump, and a pain in the stomach.

Perhaps in place of musing on oysters we should begin this chapter by remarking that Moseley's outstanding work of 1913-1915 was made possible by the fact that Wilhelm Konrad Röntgen had discovered X rays in 1895.

Röntgen, fifty years old, was at the time of his notable discovery a professor of physics with many years of research and accomplishment, but the event for which he is famous occurred in the fall of 1895. This single contribution to science vastly overshadows his other work.

From Holland, where he received his early education, Röntgen went to Zurich, Switzerland, for further studies. He received a degree in mechanical engineering from the Polytechnical School in Zurich. Pure science, meanwhile, already held a special interest for Röntgen. He began to study physics and mathematics intensively, obtaining his doctorate at the University of Zurich with a thesis, "Studies in Gases."

In Switzerland, Röntgen became interested in mountain climbing as a relaxation, and this became a lifelong hobby. He was interested also in art and music.

Röntgen's studies through the years took him to scientific work in other centers of learning, and in 1885 we see him settling down as a professor in Würzburg, Bavaria.

Throughout the years, his chief work had been on elasticity; on capillarity, the rise of liquids in narrow tubes; and on the passage of heat through crystalline substances. He had also looked into the creation, or generation, of electricity by putting pressure on certain crystals.

Röntgen also followed up on a discovery that Michael Faraday had made. Faraday discovered that a plane in which vibrations of light occur can be rotated by the application of a magnetic field. Röntgen did further work along this line.

Altogether, Röntgen was a rather experienced investigator in that year 1895—the year in which he worked on the flow of electricity in glass bulbs from which all the air had been pumped.

Many investigators turned to such problems near the close of the nineteenth century, mainly because they sought to understand the nature of electricity.

One day Röntgen was working with the apparatus illustrated here.

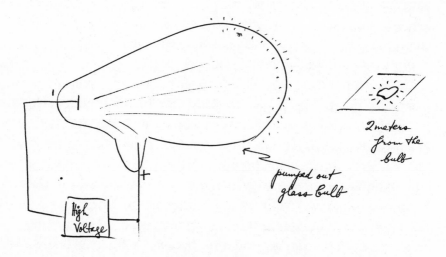

The bulb was fluorescing with an eerie green color, which was interesting enough in itself. Suddenly, Röntgen saw something shining on a nearby table. He walked over to the table and stood, completely puzzled. Why should this piece of barium platinocyanide shine, and even glow, at this remote position—a considerable distance from the glass bulb?

"Perhaps," Röntgen pondered, ". . . perhaps the greenish light from the bulb is reaching this material and exciting it to glow. Yes, that must be it."

Accordingly, he went back to the bulb and covered it with black paper. The material on that table continued to glow equally as much.

Röntgen stood staring.

He covered the glass bulb with thick black cloth. The material continued glowing. He also covered the chemicals on the table, but, peeking in, he could observe that they continued to be as much affected as they were before.

He stood examining the bulb, unbelieving.

He surrounded the glass bulb completely with thin aluminum sheets. The material on the table continued to glow! When he turned the bulb off, the barium platinocyanide stopped glowing. When he turned the bulb on again, the substance at once started to glow.

Röntgen used aluminum shielding in front of the chemicals—yet they glowed. The effect occurred through wood, books, and other barriers.

It soon became clear that, when the negative charges from the cathode struck the glass, not only did the glass fluoresce, but pulses or energy or "rays" were emitted. These rays passed directly through the glass. These "Röntgen rays" could even pass through thick slabs of metal!

In that case, why couldn't a doctor use them, for example, to find the location of a bullet in a man's leg?

He could. And, in fact, *four* days after the discovery of the Röntgen rays—or, X *rays,* since X stands for the "unknown" —a doctor actually used the technique to find the location of a bullet in the calf of a man who had been shot.

Of course, you know how the technique works. The X rays pass directly through the flesh and muscles. The rays fall upon a fluorescent screen—a screen coated with phosphorus or zinc sulfide. The X rays cause the screen to glow, or to

241

fluoresce. The bones—and bullets—stop the X rays in part, making thus a dark-shadow outline upon the screen. The outline reveals the bones or the bullet.

Röntgen thought that the rays were something that vibrated along the line of advance.

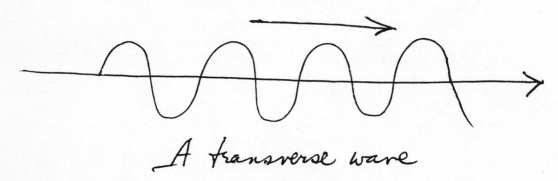

Experiments later revealed, however, the true nature of the Röntgen rays: They are *transverse* vibrations. That is, they vibrate at right angles to the path along which the rays travel. The Röntgen rays are electromagnetic in character. As such, they belong to the family of infrared rays, radio waves, and gamma rays.

X rays, as we have seen, originate as the bombarding cathode rays, or electrons, strike a solid target, such as the glass of the bulb or the positive metallic electrode. The modern X ray tubes employ more efficient sources of the electrons than did Röntgen's bulbs; we now have heftier targets than in the early days of Röntgen's research.

If we want to produce X rays of a very short wave length, the voltage V must be large, perhaps one million volts.

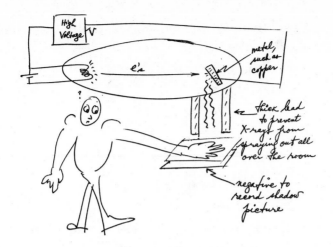

We now know that shorter wave length X rays—those of higher frequency—are more penetrating than the longer ones. The shorter ones can be used for treatment of cancer.

It all started in 1895 when Röntgen was able to report:

If the electrical discharge from a fairly large induction coil be made to pass through a Crookes tube or a Hittorf tube which has been sufficiently exhausted, fluorescence is produced in crystals of barium platinocyanide placed at distances of up to two meters away from the tube, which itself is entirely covered with black paper.

For the sake of brevity I shall use the expression "rays," and to distinguish them from others of this name, I shall call them "X rays."

We should consider further the properties of X rays:

1. They can cause fluorescence in crystals, an effect that Röntgen observed in 1895.

2. They can affect a photographic plate.

3. They can knock electrons off gas atoms, thus making the gas able to conduct electricity.

If the gas, then, is exposed to X rays, an electric current may easily flow through it.

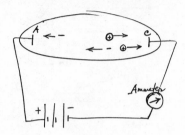

The ammeter shows current flow, as ions and electrons become a conducting link in the glass tube to complete the circuit. Without the ions and electrons, the circuit is "open," since there is no connection between A and C inside. Of course, other "agents" may help to ionize the gas, thus giving us a closed circuit.

I can't resist mentioning the following effect: If blue light, or, better still, ultraviolet light falls upon the cathode, we can get current flow.

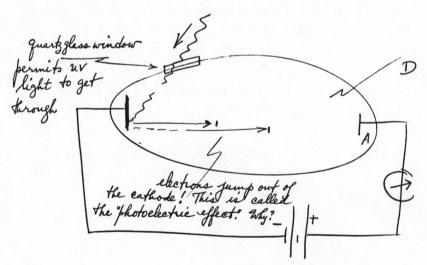

If we have gas in D, the electrons will ionize it—provided the battery voltage is high enough. If there is no gas in D, we can still get some current—the electrons liberated by the ultraviolet light.

By the way, if you shine the light upon the positive electrode *A*, you will not get the *photoelectric effect* (the liberation of electrons). Can you explain why not? I have worked for many years on problems such as these, especially where there is a gas in *D*. One of the purposes, among others, has been to investigate how well the electrons and positive ions ionize a gas. It has been extremely interesting.

Now, back to the additional properties of X rays:

4. They are very penetrating. This characteristic we have already learned. X rays can penetrate iron, lead, and anything you may try. But, some or much of their strength can be absorbed by various substances. In fact, we can stop the X rays completely if we use, say, very thick slabs of lead.

5. The rays travel through space (air, or a vacuum) with the same speed as light—186,000 miles per second. (This works out to about 30,000,000,000 cm per second, or 3×10^{10} cm/sec. Can you verify this? One inch is about 2.54 cm.)

We have already noted that the X rays are a transverse vibration, and we might say that a plane of their vibration can be changed. (Remember about light?)

6. X rays can be refracted; they can be reflected; and they can be made to produce patterns that force us to think of them as *waves*, which, after all, is the way we have been thinking up to now.

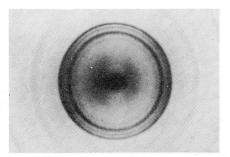

Diffraction of X-rays

PHOTOGRAPHED BY LASTOWIECKI AND GREGOR

Yet, the fact is that X rays act as particles, or *corpuscles*, in other types of interactions.

For example, consider this situation, in which X rays strike electrons:

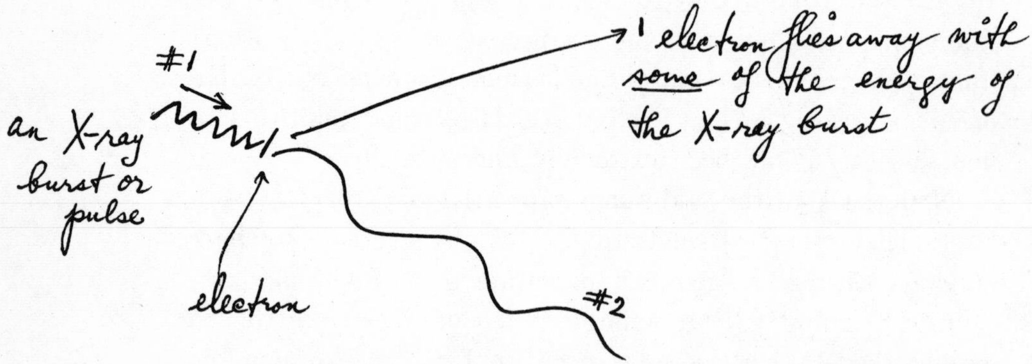

#1

an X-ray
burst or
pulse

electron

#2

electron flies away with
some of the energy of
the X-ray burst

A *longer*-wave X ray is produced. This effect accounts for the remainder of the energy of No. 1. Longer waves are less energetic than the shorter. Why?

The event described above is called the "Compton Effect," for Professor Arthur H. Compton, who discovered it, and who is one of thousands of scientists to follow through with Wilhelm Röntgen's work.

Now the *Compton Effect* is easier to sketch and to understand if we think of the X ray wave pulse as being *not quite* a wave, but, rather, a "packet," or particle, or corpuscle, or a unit—a "quantum" of energy, or an X ray "photon."

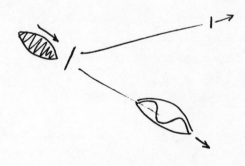

That's all I meant to say: X rays in certain experiments act as particles or corpuscles. Yet, I have included a *wave* structure too! This "duality," incidentally, is true of all of the members of the electromagnetic spectrum—radio waves, television waves, microwaves, infrared, visible light, gamma rays, X rays. . . . Incidentally, the duality is true also for *matter*. Thus, electrons, atoms, molecules, in certain interactions behave as waves, and in others they behave as corpuscles or quanta.

In almost all of our chemistry, electrons and atoms behave as *particles*. That, however, is old hat. Here, for example, is an experiment where bits of matter behave as waves.

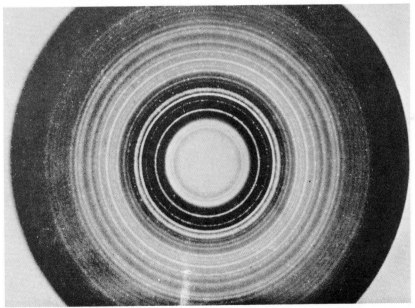

PHOTOGRAPHED BY LORIA AND KLINGER

Diffraction of Electronic Waves

Electrons passing through thin films of gold, as shown above, make wave patterns.

What shall we think, then, of radiation and matter? Which is it? Wavelike or corpuscular? Both. We note one aspect or the other of their "personality," depending upon the nature of the interaction in which they engage with other matter or radiation.

Very short X rays, incidentally, may emerge not only from the external surroundings of atoms (Remember the K and L shells, for example, in the discussion of Henry Moseley's work?) but even from the nucleus itself. This activity may occur with some radioactive nuclei, and represents merely a casting off of energy by the nucleus as it seeks to de-excite itself in attempting to become stable.

I wonder if we ought to mention some practical uses of X rays. What about these?

1. Determine if someone has tried by mixing in sand or chalk to cheat on sugar or flour. This has been done, you know, and you, as an investigator do not want to rip open every sack and taste the stuff. X rays through the sugar or flour sack will give a tell-tale pattern on a screen if there is phony stuff inside.

2. We already have mentioned pearls and oysters. I suppose it would really not be very practical to go to the market place with a portable X ray machine and look through every oyster for hidden wealth.

3. X rays can be used to differentiate between real gems and artificial ones, again by the pattern method.

4. Bombs and other dangerous materials sent by crackpots through the mails in parcels can be detected by X-raying the suspicious packages.

5. Smuggled or illegal materials can be detected by a quick X ray and fluorescent-screen inspection of the baggage.

6. In industry, flaws can be detected in metallic objects which have been cast at the foundry. Can you explain how this detection technique works?

Under "Medical" applications we already have spoken about cancer, but how about putting down this list?

7. Obtaining X ray pictures of parts of the body for diagnosis.

8. X ray treatments—tumors, pimples, ringworm. In ringworm treatment of the head, we must be very careful of the strength or dosage of the X rays. Careless use of X rays in ringworm treatment might produce baldness. Not a bald worm—but a permanent exodus of head hair of the patient.

9. X rays can produce changes in the heredity characteristics which an animal or insect will pass on to descendants. In 1928, Professor Hermann Muller produced such mutations in the genes of fruit flies. The mutations can happen also with people, with disastrous effects. This prospect is too gruesome for consideration here.

10. The dentists, of course, make frequent use of Röntgen rays, in order to make plans for your further visits to that chair.

Shall we conclude by comparing X rays with light?

Red light has a wave length of about .00008 cm.

Violet light has a wave length of about .00004 cm.

X rays may have a wave length of perhaps .00001 cm.

Much has happened since that day when Wilhelm Röntgen—the unusual scientist, apt and alert—noted the glowing of the chemicals on a table, and proceeded to investigate the phenomenon.

Many scientists have used the great discovery to rid the ill of their afflictions and to pry from nature its secrets.

Boundless benefit will yet come from the Röntgen rays.

Michelson

Albert Michelson

1852-1931

The earth is moving through space around the sun. And the sun is moving—toward the constellation Hercules, or approximately toward the star Vega. The constellation Hercules, in turn, revolves around the center of Our Galaxy. And our galaxy is running away from other galaxies. . . .

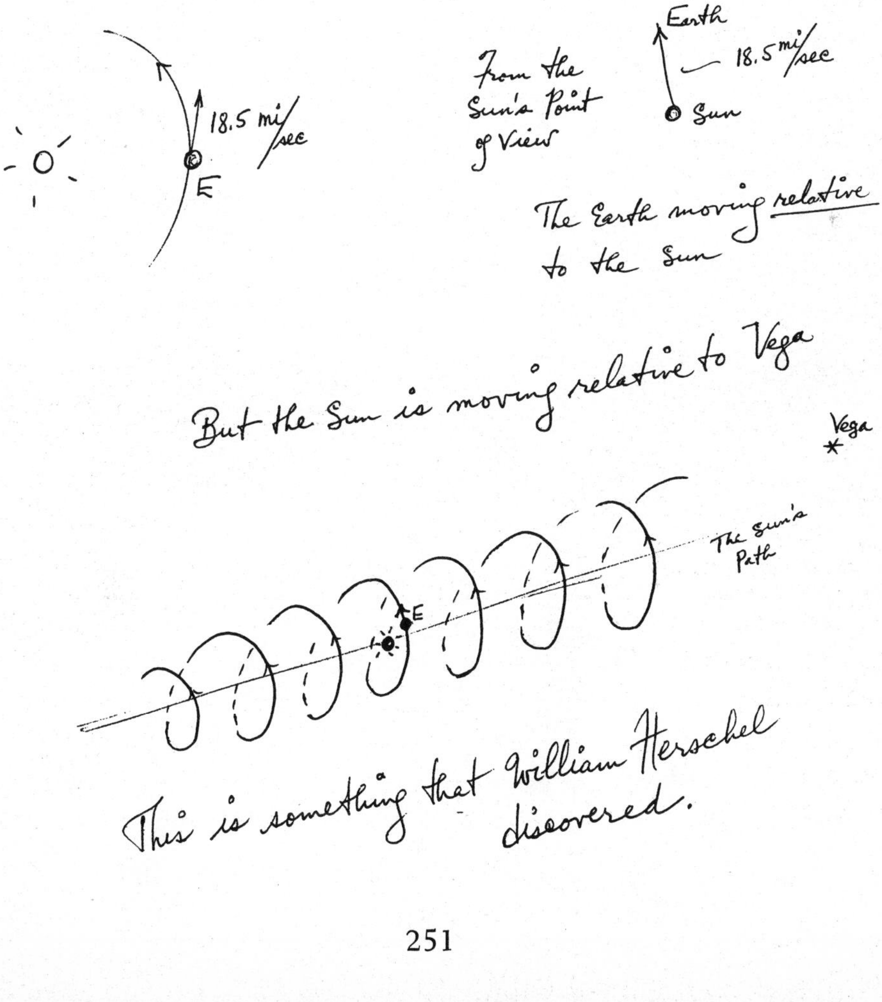

18.5 mi/sec

E

From the Sun's Point of View

Earth
— 18.5 mi/sec
Sun

The Earth moving relative to the Sun

But the Sun is moving relative to Vega

Vega
*

The Sun's Path

This is something that William Herschel discovered.

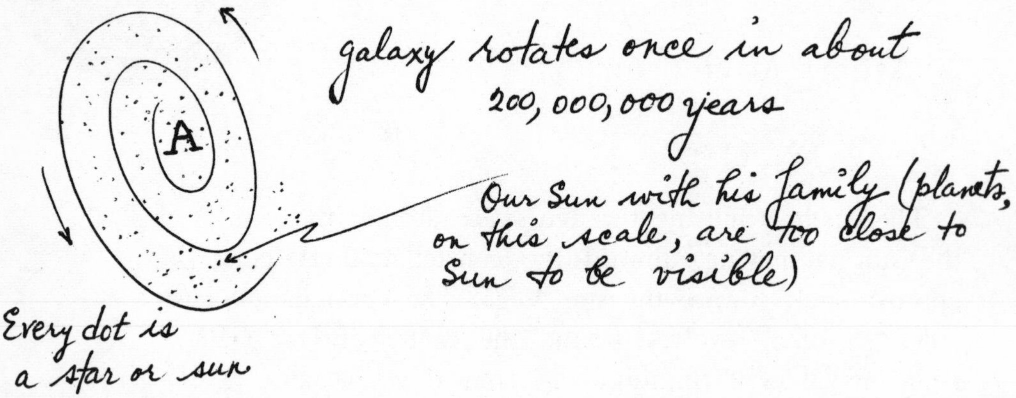

galaxy rotates once in about
200,000,000 years

Our Sun with his family (planets,
on this scale, are too close to
Sun to be visible)

Every dot is
a star or sun

If we stand at A, we would
say that B is moving away from
us. If we stand at B, we
would say, "Galaxy A
is moving away from
us."

A distant
galaxy

Well, who's *really* moving? And who's *really* standing still?

Isaac Newton believed that it made sense to speak of absolute motion and absolute space. He felt that there *was* something that was "standing still"—absolute space. Somehow, concluded Newton, we should be able to find out how earth is really moving through this absolute space.

In the nineteenth century, the physicists A. A. Michelson and E. W. Morley tried to measure earth's velocity through "absolute space," or through the "ether," as scientists began to call "it," whatever "it" was. The idea was to measure the speed of light through *something* that filled absolute space. This something was supposed to be the jelly-like "world ether," which presumably filled universal space.

If you are beginning to think that I am talking some nonsense, you are right. What is this *ether*? It is not the kind that puts you to sleep. The ether was supposed to be what we should be able to measure our motion through. (Whew!)

We were going to try to measure our *real* motion through space by observing the effect of our motion on the velocity of light. The light would be made to travel through the ether in various directions, and from this experiment we might figure out how the earth is moving through absolute space. (One scientist has said, "The ether is that which propagates our misconceptions about space from one place to another with the speed of light.")

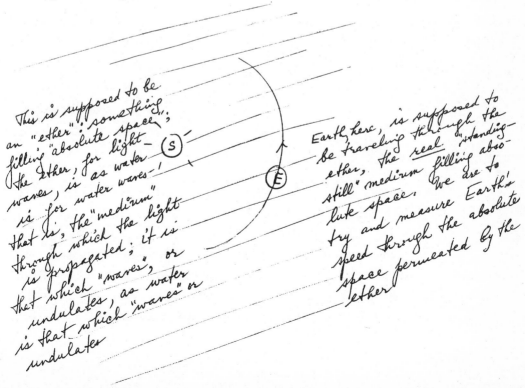

This is supposed to be an "ether": something, filling "absolute space"; the ether, for light waves, is as water waves, is for water waves—! that is, the "medium" through which the light is propagated; it is that which "waves", or undulates, as water is that which "waves" or undulates

Earth, here, is supposed to be traveling through the ether, the real "standing-still" medium filling absolute space. We are to try and measure Earth's speed through the absolute space permeated by the ether

Let us *assume* this ether, and go along with the consequences.

Since the earth moves around the sun at about 18 miles per second, we could feel or sense an ether wind, because earth is running through the ether. The ether wind would be in a direction opposite to our direction of travel, just as still air seems to blow against us as we run through it or ride through it in a car. Then, if we send a beam of light in the direction of the ether wind, the light would travel faster than it would if the earth were at rest relative to the ether wind. Obviously, this is so, since the medium—the "blowing" ether —would help the moving beam of light by carrying it along.

B ⟶ Earth going that-a-way

arrows are ether wind, in effect, blowing for *us*, in opposite direction

a beam of light (not slow) sent forward direction A has a speed of its own plus the carrying speed of the ether

A

However, a beam of light that we send in direction B would travel more slowly than normally, because it would be bucking the ether wind.

Thus it was that in 1887 Albert Abraham Michelson performed an experiment which was supposed to show the effect of our planet's motion on the velocity of light as we would measure it at the surface of the earth. Measuring the velocity of light in two directions at right angles to each other was easier for Professor Michelson than measuring it in two directions opposite to each other, and is equally as effective. Before we continue, let's work an analogous problem.

Suppose we have a boat traveling on a river, and let us say that it is to go 200 miles, between point No. 1 and point No. 2.

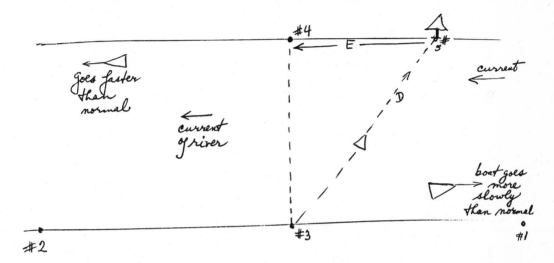

Assume that a current is flowing to the left. Then, in traveling to point No. 2, the boat goes faster than if there were no current; and, in traveling toward No. 1, it travels more slowly. The question now arises, does the trip to No. 2, with its *gain* of time, make up for the trip to No. 1, with its *loss* of time? The effects do not cancel.

For example, if the boat travels in still water at 20 mph, and if the current velocity is 5 mph, we have this: going downstream to No. 2, the boat speed will be 20 + 5, or 25 mph; going upstream to No. 1, the boat's velocity will be 20 − 5, or 15 mph. Here is the time for the round trip journey,

$$\frac{200}{25} + \frac{200}{15}, \text{ or } 8 + 13\frac{1}{3}, \text{ or 21 hours, 20 minutes}$$

If the trip is to be made *across* the river, from No. 3 to No. 4, we have to think things through before making further calculations. Do you agree that, in order to land at No. 4, we have to keep the boat pointing at an angle, a little up-stream at a point such as No. 5? Then, as the boat travels the distance No. 3 to No. 4 with velocity D, with respect to the water, it is taken downstream a distance No. 5 to No. 4, with velocity E. But E to D is in the ratio of current velocity to boat velocity,

$$\frac{E}{D} = \frac{5}{20}, \text{ or } \frac{1}{4}$$

Now we can see that to get across the river to point No. 4, we will have to travel in the direction No. 3 to No. 5, and this is *longer* than the distance No. 3 to No. 4, which would be our normal crossing distance if there were no current. In returning from No. 4, we would have to point upstream again, and our

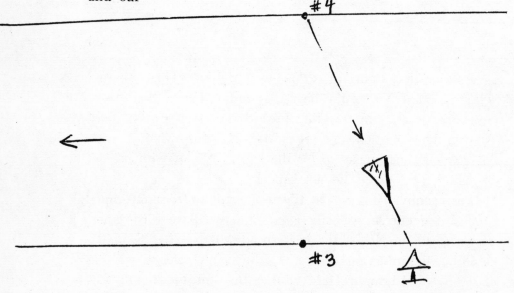

distance would once more be farther than normal. The result is this: In making a round trip *crossing* of the stream, we experience a *time delay*, as we did in going up and down stream. However, the delay in going across is less than the delay in going up and down.

We are now ready for the Michelson-Morley experiment. The river is to be replaced by the ether wind, and the boats are replaced by the traveling beams of light.

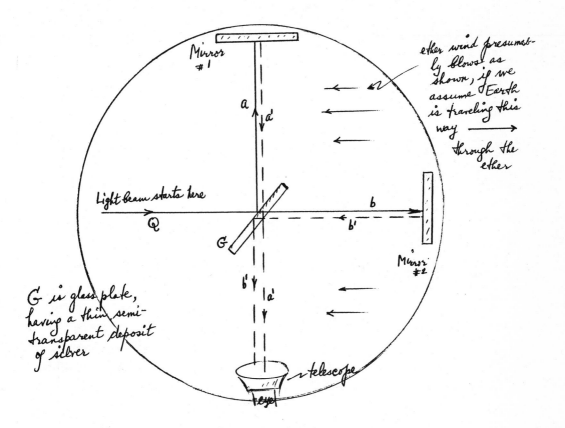

Beam *Q* divides at the lightly silvered glass plate *G;* some of the light, *a,* goes to mirror No. 1, reflects there, retraces its path; half of it goes through the silvered glass plate, and, as *a'* heads for your eye at the telescope. The second part of the original beam *Q* penetrates the silvered glass plate *G,* and as *b,* heads for mirror No. 2; it reflects there, and retraces its path as *b';* half of it reflects again at *G,* and also heads for your eye, at the telescope.

If there is no ether wind, the beams *a'* and *b'*, having traveled the same distance and done the same things, will be of equal intensity and in step.

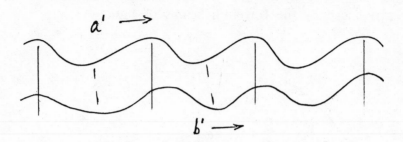

Remember, beams, or *rays*, of light are really undulations, or *waves*.

In this case, the telescope view should show brightness, as the beams re-enforce each other.

But if the earth *is* traveling through an ether, and we experience the ether wind, something different will happen. If the equipment is placed as shown, then the beam *b* and its reflection *b'* would be like the boat sailing downstream and upstream, while the beam *a* and its reflection *a'* would be like the boat sailing *across* the river and back again. Since the time delays are different for the two journeys, the beams *a'* and *b'* would not reach the telescope in step, and we would get an interfering effect there, and a consequent decrease in brightness.

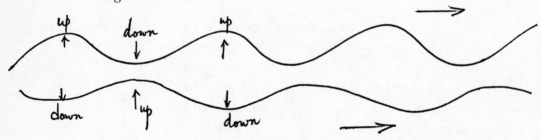

Two waves which are out of step by half of a wave length interfere with each other everywhere, and give *no* effect at all. For two such light-wave systems, we would get darkness. Of course, the waves are really very close to each other.

If we turn the equipment by 90° and thus interchange the roles of the two mirrors M_1 and M_2, we expect the same delay—whatever it was—but now in the reverse direction. Therefore, one could expect a certain total difference between the two light beams in the first and second orientations of the equipment. Moreover, one could anticipate a distinct change in the brightness of the light as one looked into the telescope and rotated the equipment through 90°. *Nothing of the kind was observed!* Scientists everywhere were certainly surprised.

It was Einstein, years later, who cast out the idea of this cooked-up ether. He also eliminated the idea of "absolute motion" through space. He spoke only about *the motion of one body relative to another body,* and he showed that the basic laws of physics should be the same everywhere—on the moon, on Mars, in another galaxy. . . . Thus was born the *Theory of Relativity.* But we will wait with that until we get to Einstein.

Albert Abraham Michelson was born in Germany in 1852. As a boy, he came with his parents to the United States, and the family settled in San Francisco. The young Michelson was able in school. He developed fast, intellectually, during the years of his advanced studies.

Michelson served as an instructor and later as a professor in a number of colleges and universities. In 1892, he became Professor of Physics and Head of the Department of Physics at the University of Chicago. He was a dedicated scientist, yet, he was interested in social problems. Michelson was an elegant dresser, and had considerable interest in the ladies. Nobody could accuse him of being a stuffed shirt.

Much can be said about his wonderful researches. For example, he measured the speed of light in a most ingenious way. His calculations were amazingly accurate.

Here is California, with Mount Wilson and Mount San Antonio, twenty-two miles apart.

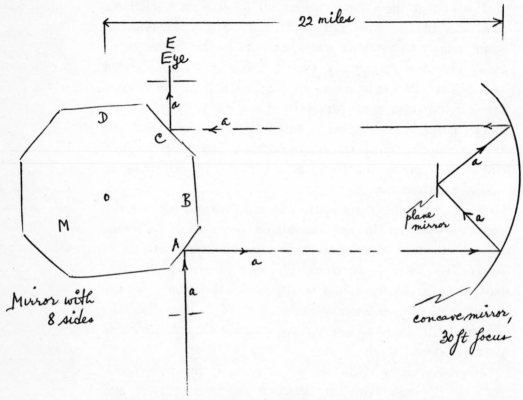

Just follow the course of the light ray *a* as it reflects from one side of the octagonal mirror. It finally arrives at your eye after passing through the slit, if all is lined up exactly right.

Now, supposing that a motor begins to rotate the octagonal mirror. After the ray *a* reflects from side *A*, do you think that you will still see light at position *E*? Not likely. I think that if the mirror is rotating slowly, then *a* will reflect from a slightly rotated side *C* and go off to one side.

But, if the mirror *M* is made to rotate faster, and just at the right speed, then this can happen: *a* will reflect from *A* as shown in the drawing, but as *a* gets back after forty-four miles of travel, side *B* will be in the position of *C*, and your beam *a* will reach your eye. Right? What does this tell us about the speed of light?

It tells us that the light took the same time to travel forty-four miles as M takes to rotate one eighth of a turn, or 45°. But we know how fast M is turning. We are rotating it with our motor, and we can easily measure the speed of the motor. In fact, M was turning at 528 revolutions per second.

Michelson had the distance between the mountains measured as accurately as possible by surveyor methods (not with a tape stretched out for twenty-two miles). The velocity of light, then, was calculated simply by dividing the *total* actual distance of travel by the time for M to make a 45° turn. The value came out 299,796 kilometers per second, which is about 186,000 miles per second.

Later, in a more accurate experiment, Michelson had the light travel through a near-vacuum pipe (air nearly all pumped out) one mile in length.

Let's have just one more experiment. I like this one.

Michelson filled an iron pipe with water to a certain level. He put microscopes at each end for use in reading the level of the water.

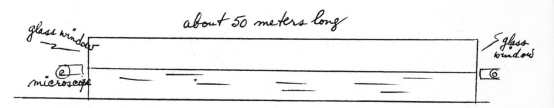

Now, he proceeded to study the tides in this device. He actually set out to measure the tidal effect of the moon and the sun. Scientists began to call this "Michelson's Ocean," and it worked!

The water surface in the pipe behaved just like the water in the oceans. At the proper times, the water surface changed its angle with respect to a fixed direction in space, responding to the gravitational pull of the moon and the sun.

But you must realize that this is a very small ocean, and so the same inclination of the water surface will give only a tiny vertical change of level at the two ends of the pipe.

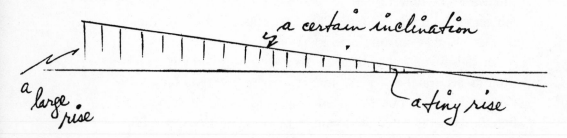

a certain inclination

a large rise

a tiny rise

With the microscopes, Michelson could detect the tiny changes of the water level. These, at most, were .0004 cm. And he was able to detect all the tidal changes of the real oceans. For example, at new moon and at full moon, Michelson detected the "exceptionally high tides" in his ocean.

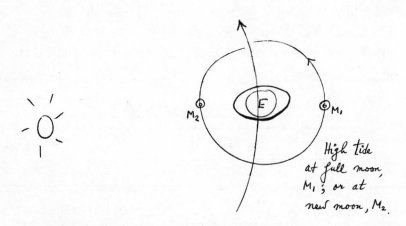

M_2

E

M_1

High tide at full moon, M_1; or at new moon, M_2.

Michelson could readily calculate how much his tides should be. He obtained only 69 per cent of the value that he had computed. But his calculations were predicting what the little tides would be if the *earth* itself did not *give,* or yield to the pull of the moon and the sun. In the experiment, he had measured the actual state of affairs—*the tide relative to the surface of the earth.* So, in view of the fact that the *rela-*

262

tive rise was only 69 per cent of the total rise predicted by theory, Michelson concluded that the missing 31 per cent was accounted for by the tidal outward swelling of the solid surface of the earth.

Since the tides in open ocean run about 75 cm, and since this is only 69 per cent of what they would be if the earth itself didn't "give" at all, the total theoretically calculated tide should be about $\frac{75}{.69}$, or 110 cm. Therefore, $110 - 75$, or 35 cm, is the measure of the tidal movement or outward swelling of the solid earth.

We must conclude, accordingly, that everything on earth— cities, mountains, and people pulse outward into space, and downward again, periodically as the moon and the sun make the earth swell and unswell. Whenever the moon in particular is high above us in the sky, we rise a little toward it, and whenever the moon heads for the horizon, we subside a little.

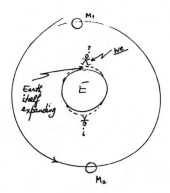

When the Moon is at M_2, we again swell outward, as the solid earth experiences another tide. So each of us swells outward into space twice a month.

Professor Michelson performed many other wonderful experiments, and invented some remarkable instruments.

He was esteemed for his excellence in work, and for his fierce devotion to the Goddess of Science. And when he laid aside his earthly cares in 1931 at the age of seventy-nine, he left a great host of inspired scientists, who have carried on.

20

Heinrich Hertz

1857-1894

Do you recall that James Clerk Maxwell predicted the existence of electromagnetic waves?

Well, Heinrich Rudolf Hertz was born in Hamburg, Germany, on February 22, 1857. And Hertz lived to discover the waves which Maxwell had predicted. His discovery laid the groundwork for the development of radio and television.

As a student, Hertz first studied architecture and engineering, but pure science and research soon interested him more than anything else. His father, a lawyer and senator of Hamburg, was of the Jewish faith, and his mother of the Lutheran. This combination in the home proved interesting to the boy, and, early in life, it taught him open-mindedness and tolerance. Joined with these qualities was an extraordinary native modesty, which never left him throughout life.

Heinrich's father was a student of languages, and a great reader of the fine literature of the world. All these interests were reflected in the boy's activities. He learned a number of languages, and developed a strong feeling for the humanities.

Moreover, Heinrich's grandfather had a great interest in the natural sciences. Over the years his grandfather had gathered some equipment, which he used in a small but fascinating laboratory of his own. Heinrich spent much time in this laboratory, helping his grandfather. When Heinrich inherited the equipment, he established his own laboratory, where he tried out some ideas in physics and chemistry.

By the time he was ready for advanced scholarship, his interests were well formulated, though at the time he thought that he wanted an engineering education. Thus it was that for one "practical year" Heinrich studied with a firm of engineers before going for a short time to the Technical High School of Dresden. Eventually, at the University of Berlin, Hertz was able to study under such outstanding scientists as Hermann von Helmholtz (1821-1894) and Gustav Kirchhoff (1824-1887). Both were famed far and wide.

Upon his graduation, Hertz was awarded the gold medal, and he later received his Doctor of Philosophy degree with the highest honors. His research for his doctorate was on the problem of inducing electrical currents in rotating spheres, work which followed up a phase of Michael Faraday's discoveries.

Hertz went in 1883 to the University of Kiel as a lecturer in theoretical physics, where he also gave himself over to the study of electromagnetism. Only two years later he was appointed Professor of Experimental Physics at the Technische Hochschule at Karlsruhe. While at Karlsruhe, he married Elizabeth Doll, the daughter of a professor. The Hertzes had two daughters, one of whom became a biochemist and the other a doctor.

This extraordinary young scientist was known as a good host, though his life was really possessed by scientific research. When he did relax from his investigations, Hertz was sociable, amiable, and genial. In the classroom he was much liked, and his students considered him a good teacher.

His consuming scientific passion in the years 1885-1889 centered on problems relating to electricity and magnetism. During this period, he first began to wonder if he could make Maxwell's prophecy come true. Hertz, outstanding in mathematics as well as in physics, was on the alert for signs of Maxwell's mathematically predicted electromagnetic waves.

Hertz followed this line of reasoning: first, one should generate electrical oscillations in a sender circuit. This should not be difficult to accomplish since *it was known* that an electrical discharge from a pair of charged metallic bodies or

266

from charged rods was not a one-way electrical current, but a fast oscillation.

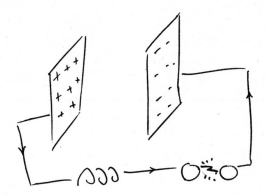

Essentially, Hertz's equipment was simple. He used an inductive coil to supply high-voltage electricity on and off ("make" and "break") to the rods *a* and *b*.

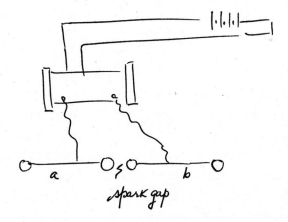

The electrical impulse from the induction coil charges up the rods *a* and *b* oppositely to very high values, until a spark

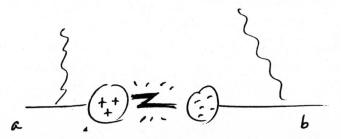

jumps across the gap. Then the electrical discharge surges back and forth along these rods, diminishing to nothing.

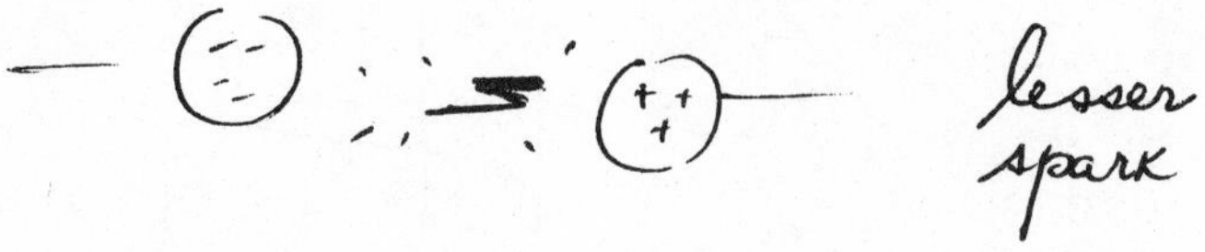

lesser spark

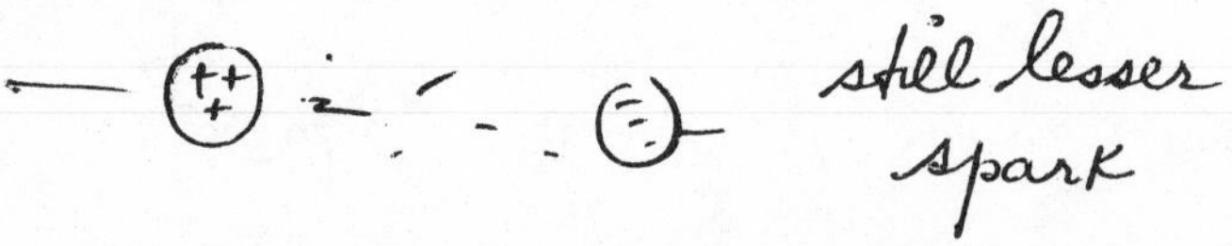

still lesser spark

Of course, the induction coil delivers another electrical impulse to the rods, whereupon the action repeats. Meanwhile, at the receiver, energy might come through space, and electrical sparks might occur.

If the induction coil keeps on supplying kicks to the sending circuit, the energy may continue to arrive at the receiving circuit.

Thus Hertz felt that such oscillations might travel away from the generator, and might be picked up by the "resonant" receiver even at some distance. The resonant receiver would be a circuit which matched the sender in design. The resonant receiver would then display its caught energy by a sparking in the gap. This procedure would be similar to sounding a tuning fork and having another fork of the *same* kind (same frequency) respond by itself.

Hertz figured out that his sender would give out with an oscillation of hundreds of millions of cycles per second. It was well known that the frequency of any oscillator depends upon the coil and condenser values, called L (self-inductance in henrys) and C (capacity in farads), like this

$$F = \frac{1}{2\pi\sqrt{LC}} \text{ cycles per second}$$

268

His first experiment was set up in the physics lecture auditorium, with the receiver at one end and the sender at the other. He darkened the auditorium, and, breathless, watched the gap of the receiver. Suddenly, tiny sparks appeared! This was it. So Maxwell had been right. What a pity he had not lived to see his prophecy substantiated.

In a word, what he found was this: electricity surging back and forth in one circuit could somehow detach itself and appear in another circuit, which might even be in another room.

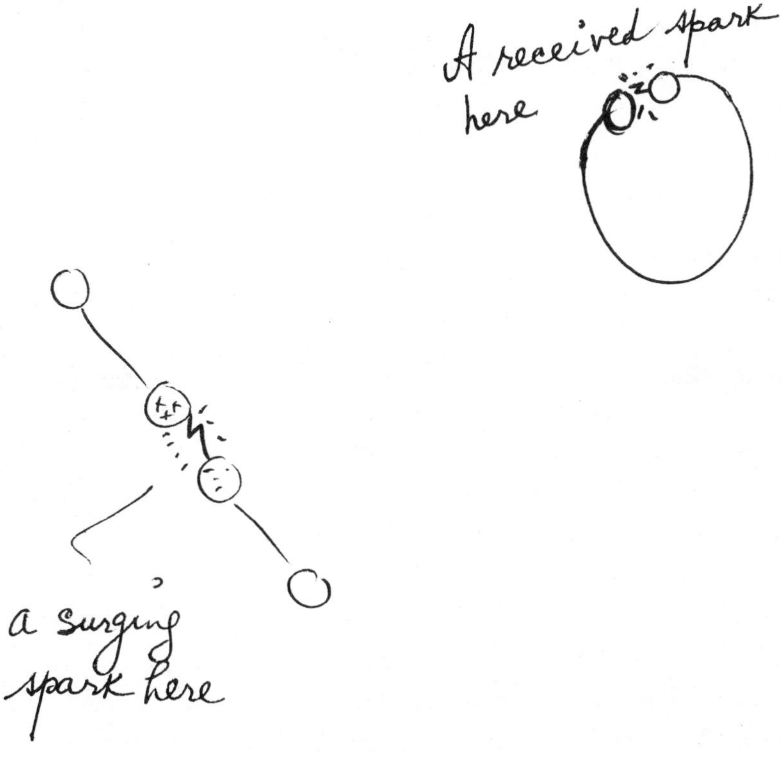

A received spark here

a surging spark here

Hertz, in subsequent experiments with improved apparatus, took his receiver into an adjacent room behind closed doors. The invisible waves came through, induced current in the receiver, and made sparks! Hertz was in ecstasy.

Later, he spoke of the event in this way, "Insulators do not stop the ray. It passes right through a wooden partition or door; and it is not without astonishment that one sees the sparks appear inside a closed room."

The other day I repeated this experiment, going far away into another room. It is yet to this day exciting to see the indicator show that the waves are coming through.

Yet, Hertz still had to prove that the radiated energy is like *light*—this was part of Maxwell's theory: the predicted waves should travel with the speed of light; it should be possible to reflect them, to refract them, to change their plane of vibration.

After many trials and disappointments, Hertz worked out a large apparatus of this kind:

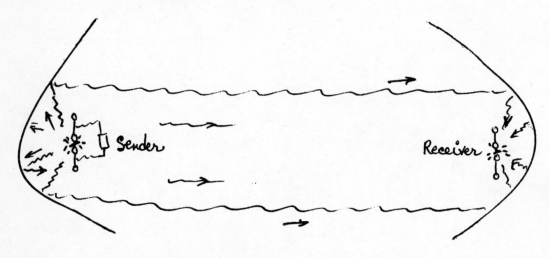

It worked. A spark appeared across the gap of the receiver. The waves from the sender apparatus at the focus struck the metallic parabolic mirror, were reflected in parallel beams, and then were refocused by the second mirror, thus concentrating the waves upon the receiver at the second focus. At first he had not been successful because the waves he had produced were of too long a wave length. The waves must not be long compared with the size of the metallic mirror.

It was possible also to get reflections of this type:

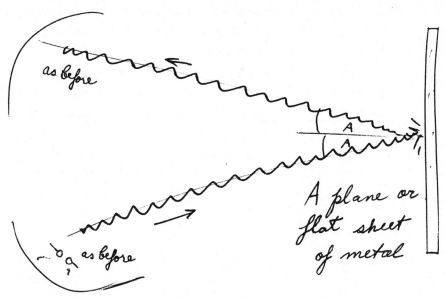

as before

A

A plane or
flat sheet
of metal

as before

Actually, this is exactly the way light behaves. The angle of incidence is equal to the angle of reflection.

Hertz then worked on refraction:

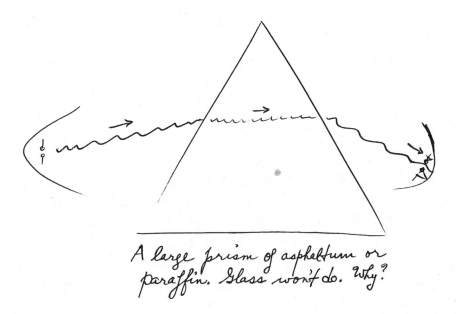

A large prism of asphaltum or
paraffin. Glass won't do. Why?

Maxwell's waves could be bent, just as happens with light.

Now, how to determine the speed of the waves? Their speed should be the same as that of light. Hertz reasoned this way: If one end of a rope is tied to a wall, and, if we keep snapping the other end just right, we can get a wave traveling down the rope, reflecting at the wall and returning to interfere with the forward wave. The interference can give "standing waves."

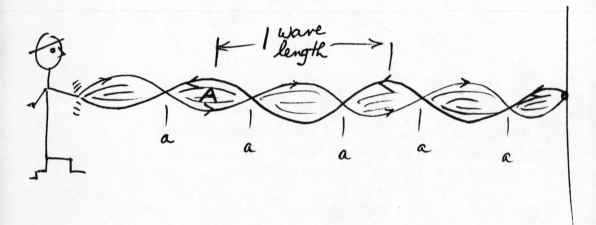

The net effect is a loop such as A, swelling and unswelling.

Yet, the position of the pattern remains constant. That is, the points a remain inactive, whereas the middle of a loop is full of motion and upward or downward kick, giving a blurred or fuzzy view as the rope pulses and unpulses there.

So Hertz tried this with the Maxwellian electrical waves. In order to detect points of maximum activity, he used the receiver resonator without its parabola.

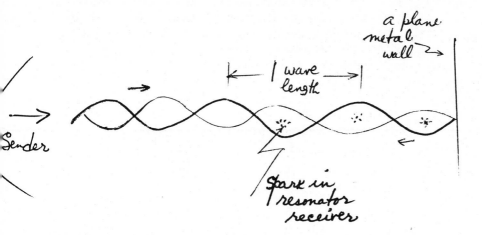

As he carried the resonator receiver from the wall to the left, he did get a spark! Then, as he proceeded, he got nothing. Then, further along, he obtained another spark! Again nothing. Then again a spark. It worked. So he had produced standing electromagnetic waves, and he had the wave length!

Now what? He knew the frequency (oscillations per second) of the generator. (Remember the formula for *F*? Also, the frequency could be determined by experiment.) Thus, he had the *distance* that the wave travels in the known *time* of one complete oscillation. If he divided these two figures—that is, the distance by the time—he would get the speed of the waves. Hertz breezed through the calculation: *The speed of light!* About 186,000 miles per second. . . .

His joy almost knew no bounds.

In his report to the Association for Advancement of Science at Heidelberg, in 1889, Hertz said,

We observe that in certain places, there are sparks at the gap *G*, but at others, none; we see that the dead points follow each other periodically in ordered succession. Thus, the propagation in time is proved and the wave length can be measured. . . . We multiply the wave length by the calculated frequency of oscillations and find a velocity which is about that of light. . . .

273

The connection between light and electricity . . . is now established
. . . In every flame, in every luminous particle, we see an electrical
process. Even if a body is not luminous, provided it radiates heat, it is
a center of electrical disturbances. Thus, the domain of electricity ex-
tends over the whole of nature. It even affects ourselves intimately: we
perceive that we actually possess an electrical organ—the eye. . . ."

Hertz, I might say, was also the first man to come upon the
photoelectric effect, though he did not understand its significance. He had discovered that ultraviolet light from the spark
could trigger sparks in the receiver—the spark there passed
more easily.

What is more, Hertz barely missed discovering X rays. In
fact, he missed by a hair's breadth. He had been working on
electricity in rarefied gases and had observed the cathode rays,
though he did not know that they were electrons (electrons
were not yet known). He observed how the glass fluoresced

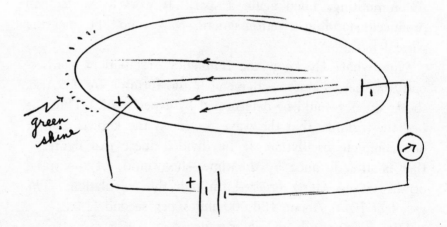

with an eerie greenish light when the tube operated. He even
observed something pass directly through the glass and
through thin strips of metal. He was *almost* upon the yet-
undiscovered X rays.

He was, however, at about the end of the line. He was only
thirty-seven. Yet, he had cancer. He had cancer of the bone,
and an operation was too late.

Hertz dragged himself to work. Unable to get around much in the laboratory, he concentrated on pencil and paper—on theoretical work.

He continued to lecture until December 1893.

"These are the ultimate problems of physical science," he had written, "the icy summits of its loftiest range. Shall we ever be permitted to set foot upon one of those summits? . . . the first steps that we see form a gentle ascent, and among the rocks, there are tracks leading upwards. There is no lack of eager and practiced explorers: how can we feel otherwise than hopeful of the success of future attempts?"

There were no more attempts for him.

He died on January 1, 1894, at the age of thirty-seven.

During a brief life he had stood on the shoulders of James Clerk Maxwell. And he had found Maxwell's waves.

Would someone else come along to put these waves to work for communication purposes? You know that someone did come along—Marconi. Lee De Forest (1873-1961) and others, too, came along. And so, today we have radio and television.

Maxwell predicted the waves by mathematics; Hertz produced them; Marconi put them to work.

How I wish that the noble Maxwell had lived to see his waves a reality, and that the devoted, hard-working Heinrich Hertz had lived only a little longer to see the electromagnetic waves put to use serving humanity.

Curie

21

Marie and Pierre Curie

1867-1934, 1859-1906

In 1896, the French scientist Henri Becquerel (1852-1908) discovered that the element uranium emits strange and penetrating rays. Uranium itself had been known since 1789, when it was discovered by Martin Heinrich Klaproth (1743-1817). Yet, no one had known of its amazing rays.

Becquerel had left a piece of uranium ore in the same drawer with a photographic plate placed in a black envelope. Later, thinking that he had exposed the plate, Becquerel developed it. To his amazement, a dark spot showed up on the negative.

Becquerel suspected the uranium ore. He began a series of experiments which showed that uranium was a constant emitter. Becquerel made some very striking pictures as he warmed to his subject.

He placed a metal key on a photographic plate, and put the key and the plate in a dark, light-proof envelope. Then he placed some uranium ore atop the envelope. Later, he developed the plate, and found an image of the key on the negative. Clearly, rays from the uranium had passed directly through the key and had made the picture.

You can imagine how excited everyone was. Only recently, in 1895, Röntgen had discovered X rays to be penetrating rays, and here was the discovery of other powerful rays. These other rays came from a mineral rather than from a glass tube in which fast cathode rays were produced.

A young Polish girl, Manya Sklodowska, had come to Paris for advanced scientific studies, and also to get away from a somewhat repressive political regime. For a long time she had waited for her chance to begin these studies, biding her time while her older sister Bronya studied abroad to become a physician. Manya—or Maria—helped to support Bronya, sending her what money she could spare from her meager earnings at home as a tutor and governess.

Now, however, it was 1896, and Maria or Marie, as she was known in Paris, began her studies. At first, she had a difficult time. She was short of money, and often hungry. But, in spite of all such handicaps, her studies went on.

Marie advanced in her work. Soon she realized that more than anything else she wanted to be a research scientist. But what problem should she investigate? She explored several possibilities. Then, upon learning of Becquerel's discovery, she knew what her work was to be. She would investigate all the elements, to see whether any besides uranium gave out rays.

How can we tell whether a substance gives out rays, that is, whether it is *radioactive?*

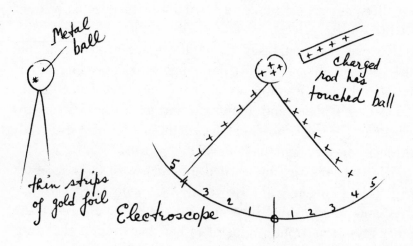

An electroscope consists of a metal ball from which two thin strips of gold foil are suspended. The gold strips move away from each other when a charged rod touches the ball.

278

The gold strips, you see, take on the charge, let's say a plus charge. As you know, like charges repel each other. Thus, the strips move away. In the drawing (page 278), the strips are about eight divisions apart.

Now, let us bring some uranium close to the electroscope. The rays from the uranium break up many atoms of the air surrounding the electroscope. Negative charges from these atoms drift toward the positively charged foils. Gradually, the gold strips are neutralized. Accordingly, the foils repel each other with less force. Responding to gravity, they move in toward each other.

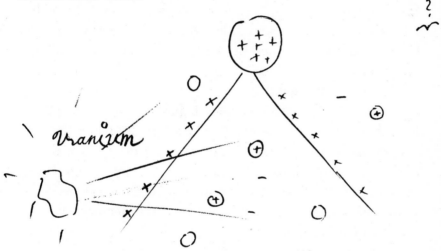

Thus, from the rate of the collapse of the gold strips, we can learn how strong the uranium sample is. By just such a method, Marie learned that thorium, too, emits rays.

In 1898, after a long examination of various ores, Marie discovered a new substance which emitted rays, a *new* element, which she named "polonium" in honor of her native land.

Meanwhile, Marie met a young professor, Pierre Curie. Pierre had already made a name for himself in research, particularly in the study of crystals and how pressure generates electrical effects on some of them.

Pierre was tall, sedate-looking with a beard. His eyes were deep-set and serene; the face seemed relaxed, rested. His clothes were sober, comfortable, old-fashioned. People said that Pierre had a natural elegance, and this seemed to be accentuated by his long and sensitive hands.

Marie was blonde, blue-eyed, bright-looking, yet endowed with an appealing shyness, and possessed of a deep seriousness of purpose. Some people spoke of her precision, iron will, and "incredible stubbornness."

Pierre loved to talk to her. He found it strange but satisfying to be able to discuss the work he loved with a woman. There was no coquetry. But, to Pierre, how beautiful was her hair. How smoothly curved her forehead. And her hands. They were feminine hands, delicately formed. But stained with acid.

They were married.

The marriage was an extremely happy one. Marie displayed many feminine traits, some of which caught Pierre by surprise. She could be childish or distant and deep, all within a brief interval of time. Yet, she had this inflexibility—her resolute and steadfast determination to make good on three fronts: toward her husband, science, and motherhood.

She had a child—Irene.

"Women of genius are rare," Pierre used to say.

It was abundantly clear that he had come upon such a one. She was stubborn. But her stubbornness was directed principally against nature—against the scientific goals she set for herself. This trait, in time, revealed itself for all the world to see.

Pierre, like Marie, was stubborn. But it was in his research and never in a situation to advance himself that he displayed this quality. He disliked, for example, being a candidate for any position, and on several occasions he praised his rival to a selection committee. Unfortunately, the committee believed the sincere Pierre and they did in fact appoint the competitor.

Perhaps it might have been well for Pierre to have reflected on Montaigne's remark, "With great merit and even greater modesty, one can remain unknown for a long time."

Pierre devoted his life to science and to his wife.

"When we work in science," he reminded his students, "any discovery that we may make, however small, will remain acquired knowledge."

In carrying out their research, the Curies separated uranium from the mineral pitchblende. Marie, one day, came across an astonishing phenomenon. She discovered that a radioactive material remained in the pitchblende after the uranium was removed. This unidentified material, in fact, gave off much more powerful rays than uranium itself!

Marie and Pierre Curie set out to track down this substance. The work was involved and exhausting. It went on for month after month. Thus, the early period of their marriage was an arduous one. But the work was rewarding.

On April 12, 1898, Marie Sklodowska Curie announced the probable presence of a new element in pitchblende ores. She made the announcement at a scientific meeting. This new element, she explained, possessed enormous radioactive powers.

Marie and Pierre continued with their work. They separated all the elements in pitchblende by regular chemical analysis. Then they measured the radioactivity of each of the materials extracted.

Yet, a certain component—the most powerful radioactive material of all—kept eluding them. It showed up in only tiny amounts. The Curies lacked enough pitchblende to obtain significant quantities of the mysterious material. Accordingly, they sent for *tons* of pitchblende, and began to "boil" all of it down.

Pierre and Marie had come to believe thoroughly in the existence of this mysterious element. They even gave it a name. They called it "radium."

Now, the Curies were on the spot. Scientists everywhere took the attitude, "You named it—now prove it. Get it."

Marie and Pierre were persistent. For four struggling years, they boiled down pitchblende from the St. Joachimstahl Mines in Bohemia. They worked doggedly and with confidence, refusing to become discouraged.

The day came. They had it. It was shining in the dark with a beautiful glow. It was a tremendously radioactive bit of material—one tenth of a gram of pure *radium.*

Marie determined its atomic weight—it was about 226.

Here is the structure of radium, as we know it today:

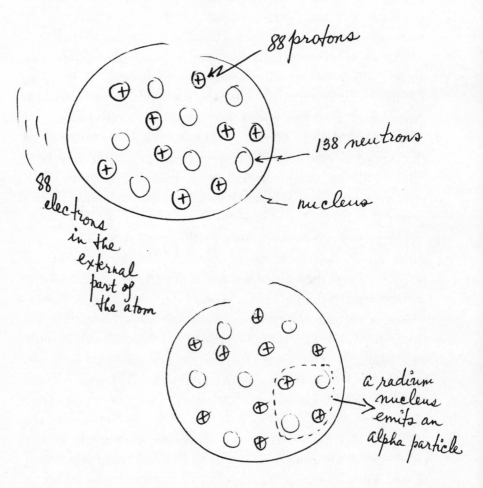

After the radium nucleus emits an alpha particle, the remaining nucleus has only 86 protons, with the result that it is a nucleus of *radon*, a different element. Radon, in turn, emits an alpha particle, and becomes *polonium*. And so the process continues, with an alpha particle, a gamma ray, or a fast electron—the beta particle—coming out.

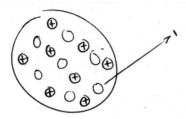

The beta particle comes out when a neutron within a radioactive nucleus emits it; that is, emits an electron. The neutron thereby becomes a proton. As a result, the nucleus goes up one in atomic number. A different element has evolved. Radium descends from uranium in this way. We'll take up the sequence of events in a later chapter.

We might say a few more words about radium itself:

1. One gram of pure radium emits 3.7×10^{10} alpha particles per second (37,000,000,000).

2. If we have 1,000,000 radium atoms today, we will have only 500,000 in about 1,600 years. And after another 1,600 years, we'll have only 250,000. . . . We say, "The half-life of radium is about 1,600 years."

3. The energy from radium is about 1,000,000 times greater than that from an equal weight of chemical reactants. With its descendants, radium gives us about 1,236,000 calories per gram.

4. The speed of the emerging alpha particles is about 10,000 miles per second. The beta particles, from subsequent elements, come sailing out at about 50,000 miles per second.

To get only one gram of radium, a firm might use about

one hundred tons of mineral (pitchblende and associated ores). Hence, we can appreciate the magnitude of the job Marie and Pierre Curie slaved over for four years.

One property of radium points up the importance of Marie Curie's discovery. Its rays can be used for treating cancer.

The news spread.

A world-wide demand for this life-saving material suddenly developed. Marie and Pierre Curie considered patenting the complex process of extraction. They would make an enormous fortune for themseves, millions of dollars. They decided against patenting. They gave the method free to the world.

"Radium belongs to the people," said Marie.

The honors began to come in. Someone wanted to decorate Pierre with a medal and a sash. He told the messenger, "Please be kind enough to thank the minister, but tell him that I feel not the slightest need of a decoration, but I have very great need for a laboratory."

Marie and Pierre returned to their laboratory and to their research. Between the years 1899 and 1904, the husband and wife team published thirty-two scientific papers.

They had a second daughter, Eve.

Then, on April 19, 1906, occurred a tragic accident. Pierre was crossing a street. He fell in front of a horse-drawn wagon. The heavy wheels rolled over him, and he was killed.

Pierre had been lecturing on physics, and his last lecture ended on the theme that the class would consider "the progress in physics of the last ten years. . . ."

The Sorbonne in Paris appointed Marie to Pierre's professorial position. When she entered the hall for her first lecture, she began with the words,

"When we consider the progress made in physics in the last ten years . . ."

And so life went on. But a silent sadness encompassed Marie. As the years passed, and honors poured in upon her, the sadness remained. A humility remained. A simplicity remained.

Einstein said of her, "Marie Curie is the one person I know who does not know how to be famous."

Marie carried on as chief of operations in the laboratory at the Sorbonne. This was the post that had been created for Pierre. She did a great deal, moreover, to establish a laboratory of radioactivity in Poland, the country of her birth, at Warsaw. During World War I, she drove an ambulance to help save the fallen soldiers.

The Curies—Marie and Pierre—received the 1903 Nobel prize in physics, along with Henri Becquerel, for their work in isolating radium and polonium. In 1911, Marie received her second Nobel prize, this time in chemistry for determining the chemical properties of radium and for isolating it in a pure state by passing an electric current through molten radium chloride. She is the only scientist, man or woman, ever to receive two Nobel prizes.

Marie Curie died at the age of sixty-seven, worn out from her labors and debilitated by overexposure, throughout the years, to the rays which have saved thousands of lives.

And here is an event of note. On the shoulders of Marie Curie stood her own daughter, Irene, who became a great physicist, and who, like her mother, married a scientist, Fréderic Joliot (1900-1958).

Irene, too, received a Nobel prize, for discovering *artificial* radioactivity.

Irene's life, likewise, was cut short by the radioactive rays, and, in her early fifties, she died of leukemia.

They gave the full measure. And the world will never forget.

The woman who did not know how to be famous will be remembered as long as atomic nuclei emit rays, and as long as people are healed by these rays in all the hospitals of Planet Earth.

Rutherford

22

Ernest Rutherford

1871-1937

I've been reading about the alchemists—you know, those men who were part scientists, part sleight-of-hand artists, who tried to make gold out of lead or mercury. In general, they tried to make one element out of another.

These alchemists were at work as far back as about 2,000 years, and they were especially active in the Middle Ages. I suppose today their methods of operation would remind you of the witches in Macbeth—mumbo-jumbo, and the steaming cauldron. Some of them, of course, were sincere chemical investigators. Some, however, were charlatans.

Many of them said they were seeking, first, the so-called "Philosopher's Stone" by which they could then change the "baser metals" to gold or silver. Look at the painting which shows an alchemist dropping a large scorpion into his brew. If nothing else would produce gold, supposedly the scorpion surely would come through.

CULVER PICTURES, INC.

In the city of Oxford, England, near the University, there is a large building which contains in the basement some of the laboratories of the alchemists. When I visited there several years ago, I found it to be an eerie place, fascinating and exciting. Much equipment still remains, and there are gloomy recesses in the walls. The structure now is largely given over to a science museum, yet I think that the basement remains the most interesting part.

The Alchemists, as you know, did not succeed in producing gold from any other substance. Finally, everyone, including the genuine scientists, concluded that changing one element into another was utterly impossible.

Now, let's turn to someone who was destined to come to this Oxford area. Let's go to New Zealand. Find the map, and look for the town of Nelson. Near this town, in the community called "Brightwater," in the year 1871 a boy was born to a family of pioneer stock. The parents had come many years previously from the British Isles. The father, whose name was James Rutherford, had built the house in which the boy was born.

The father was a very resourceful man, a builder, a farmer, a kind of jack-of-all trades out in wild, new territory. He was a "bush engineer," people said of him, admiringly. He raised flax, built mills, and constructed bridges. The mother of the boy was a sensitive woman, musical, a teacher, and the manager of a large family of children. There were twelve children in all.

The boy whom we have in mind was named Ernest. He was the fourth-born in the family. Even at an early age he proved to be as resourceful as was his father.

Ernest was daring and imaginative. As for schooling, he went to the Havelock Primary School, Nelson High School, which was called Nelson College, and later to Canterbury University College, a branch of the University of New Zealand. In all of his schools, Ernest was fortunate in having devoted and inspiring teachers, for these pioneers laid much stress on education.

Ernest became interested in physics and mathematics. At the University, he began to experiment, and his first trials were in magnetization of iron in rapidly alternating fields. He also developed a device which could detect the Hertzian and Maxwellian electromagnetic waves, which we have already considered.

BROWN BROTHERS

Here is a photograph of Ernest Rutherford at an early age. He seems eager and determined. Ernest had met an attractive young girl named Mary Newton, about whom we shall hear more, later.

Ernest Rutherford won a scholarship to Cambridge University in England. He left for Cambridge in 1895. There he worked under a very great physicist, J. J. Thomson (1856-1940).

These were exciting days in physics. Late in 1895, remember? Röntgen, in Germany, discovered X rays. Becquerel, in France, discovered radioactivity in early 1896. By 1897, Thomson himself recognized the corpuscular nature of electricity—those negative particles we call electrons.

So it was that, although Ernest had started his research work at Cambridge with Hertzian waves, continuing his New Zealand work, he soon jumped into the new discoveries, especially into the investigation of how uranium electrifies the air. Ernest soon became completely absorbed in his work, visualizing the creation of the tiny particles of electrification so clearly that he wrote to a friend, "Ions are jolly little beggars; you can almost see them."

He wrote regularly to his mother in New Zealand and to Mary Newton.

As he continued his experimental work, he came to be recognized as a brilliant experimenter. At this time, a medical man who knew him, Dr. Henry Balfour, wrote to a friend, "We've got a rabbit here from the Antipodes and he's burrowing mighty deep."

In fact, Ernest burrowed so deep that within three years he received an offer of a professorship at McGill University in Montreal, Canada. He accepted. Upon his arrival there, he continued his work on radiations emitted by uranium and radium. Marie Curie was able to send him an adequate supply of radium.

Rutherford discovered that the radiations were complex in character. He determined that one type consisted of very energetic positively charged particles, which he named "alpha" particles, and another type of radiation consisted of negatively charged particles. These negative particles were much smaller in mass than the alpha particles, but they moved much more rapidly, and Ernest named them "beta" particles. He measured their speed and their ability to electrify gases.

There was also another type of radiation, recognized later, which we call "gamma" rays. Today, we might visualize these various particles and the gamma rays somewhat in this manner:

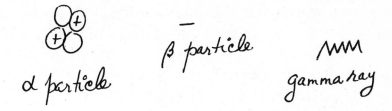

α particle β particle gamma ray

In 1900, Ernest returned to New Zealand to wed Mary Newton, and with her returned to Montreal. Their daughter was born about a year later. The Rutherfords named their little girl Eileen. She was their only child.

While at McGill, Ernest received competent assistance from Hans Geiger, a German scholar, and from William Kay, who was very able with instruments of all types. Geiger was the man who invented the device, the Geiger Counter, which can detect single particles such as alphas and betas and can be arranged to make a click for each one. . . . click, click, click.

Researchers at McGill also used an instrument called the Wilson Cloud Chamber. With this device, one can see or even photograph the path followed by an alpha particle or a beta particle as it penetrates some saturated vapor. You can look up the Wilson Cloud Chamber. It is an interesting scientific device.

A brilliant young chemist named Frederick Soddy (1877-) arrived from Oxford. Ernest Rutherford and Soddy worked as a team in attempting to understand what happened in the various processes of radioactivity. By 1902, Rutherford and Soddy were able to formulate a theory regarding "radioactive transformation" dealing with this new idea: When a radioactive atom emits an alpha or a beta particle, the atom becomes transformed into a different atom; such atoms are able to transform themselves, to transmute themselves.

Thus, since one element does change into another, nature is an alchemist. In 1907, Rutherford with his family moved to Manchester University in England. There he continued his work with radioactive substances. In 1908, Ernest received a Nobel prize. Interestingly enough, the award was in chemistry and not in physics. These two fields, however, overlap considerably in certain areas.

Rutherford now studied what happens when alpha particles are used to bombard various substances. He was using the alpha particles as probes to learn the nature of the atomic structure of the probed or bombarded element. The alpha particles were scattered through various angles.

The most startling result of this type of work was the fact that sometimes the very energetic alpha particles would bounce straight back from even very thin metallic foils. When the young research man, Marsden, who had been set on this project by Rutherford, reported the results, Rutherford was amazed. He said, "It's as if one had fired a fifteen-pound shell at a piece of tissue paper and the shell bounced back at you."

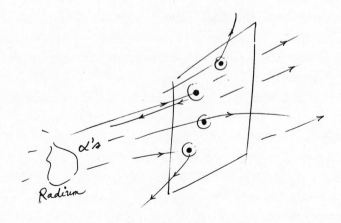

Here, then, is how Rutherford visualized that the scattering and the bouncing back took place:

Remember, the alpha particle is positively charged, and it is now being repelled by the positive charge of the atom. Thus, Rutherford decided that the bombarded atoms were largely empty space and that nearly all of the material, mass, was concentrated in tiny points at the centers of the atoms. All of the positive charge of the atom, he concluded, was also concentrated at these tiny points in the centers of the atoms.

Thus, Rutherford formulated the idea of a *nuclear atom*. There were, on the outside of the atom, circulating electrons to balance the positive charge of the nucleus. The theory of Niels Bohr (1885-   ), the Danish physicist, helped on this problem, and the research of Henry Moseley, as you know, helped to establish the amount of positive charge on the nuclei of various elements.

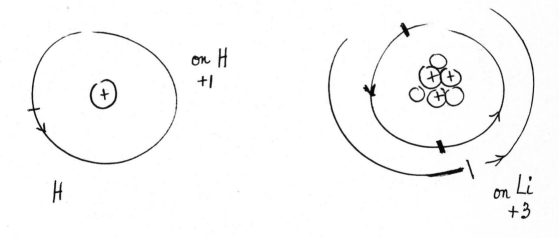

People were now beginning to call Rutherford's atom a "solar system atom." The nucleus was like the sun and the electrons were like the planets. And, in fact, Rutherford is often thought of as "The Newton of the Atom." He liked this. He once wrote, "I know of no more enthralling adventure than this voyage of discovery into the almost unexplored world of the atomic nucleus."

Ernest devoted himself to the work of his laboratory so thoroughly that external events meant little to him at this time. When a friend, Professor W. H. Bragg (1862-1942) wrote for his advice on whether or not he should accept the presidency of a university, Ernest replied, "The exalted positions of the world have very little attraction—at any rate to me."

On another occasion, when he learned that he was to be knighted, he wrote to the Hungarian chemist George von Hevesy (1885-   ), who had extended his congratulations "I trust that it will not interfere with my future activities."

By now, through the work of a number of scientists, the radioactive transformations were understood in considerable detail:

When an atom emits an alpha particle, the atom becomes a new one, four points less in mass number, and two points less in positive charge. When the atom emits a beta particle, it remains essentially unchanged in mass, but one point higher in positive charge. In this way, uranium, for example, goes through successive changes, one element changing into another, until the element lead is reached. Like this:

$$U \xrightarrow{\alpha} Th \xrightarrow{\beta} Pa \xrightarrow{\beta} U \xrightarrow{\alpha} Th \xrightarrow{\alpha} Ra \xrightarrow{\alpha} Rn \xrightarrow{\alpha} Po \xrightarrow{\alpha} Pb \xrightarrow{\beta} Bi \xrightarrow{\beta} Po \xrightarrow{\alpha}$$

$$\xleftarrow{\beta} Pb$$
$$\xleftarrow{\alpha} Bi$$
$$\xleftarrow{\beta} Tl$$
$$Pb \xleftarrow{}$$

The end of the line

Or, more fully

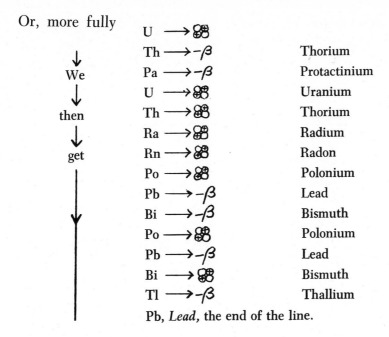

U	→	
Th	→ −β	Thorium
Pa	→ −β	Protactinium
U	→	Uranium
Th	→	Thorium
Ra	→	Radium
Rn	→	Radon
Po	→	Polonium
Pb	→ −β	Lead
Bi	→ −β	Bismuth
Po	→	Polonium
Pb	→ −β	Lead
Bi	→	Bismuth
Tl	→ −β	Thallium

We

then

get

Pb, *Lead,* the end of the line.

Along with the beta emission, we usually get gamma rays, γ, coming out, too. It is the gamma rays that are useful in burning off cancer.

Or, starting with uranium,

$$\alpha\ \beta\ \beta\ \alpha\ \alpha\ \alpha\ \alpha\ \alpha\ \beta\ \beta\ \alpha\ \beta\ \alpha\ \beta$$

The coming of the first World War caused a considerable scattering of Rutherford's laboratory staff. Hans Geiger returned to his native Germany to become an artillery officer, Marsden left to fight for the Allies, Moseley was killed at Gallipoli, and Ernest Rutherford worked on submarine detection problems at home. When he could, Rutherford continued his research with the help of William Kay. Now, during the years 1917 to 1919, Ernest Rutherford, in fact, was on the trail of a great event. First, we must state that he had been able to show that alpha particles are the nuclei of helium atoms.

Now the great event was this: Rutherford allowed alpha particles to bombard nitrogen gas. The result was that nitrogen was changed into oxygen. Let us look at a diagram of the equipment, *below,* and see how the process is carried out.

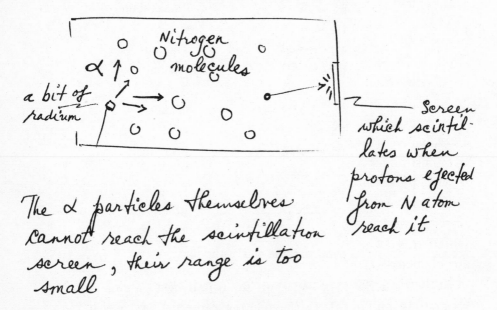

a bit of radium

Nitrogen molecules

Screen which scintillates when protons ejected from N atom reach it

The α particles themselves cannot reach the scintillation screen, their range is too small

I saw this apparatus at Cambridge a few years ago. It is simple, but nonetheless ingenious. Here is the reaction that takes place in the experiment:

$$_2He^4 + {_7}N^{14} \rightarrow {_8}O^{17} + {_1}H^1$$

The $_1H^1$ flies away, striking a zinc sulfide screen and making a flash. Here, then, we have a nitrogen nucleus capturing the alpha particle. Remember that the alpha is a helium nucleus. The hydrogen nucleus—named "proton" by Rutherford—chips away, and goes flying. The nitrogen nucleus, with the captured alpha particle but minus that departed hydrogen nucleus, is now an oxygen nucleus.

The subscripts refer to the positive charges on the nuclei and the superscripts refer to the number of total particles in each nucleus. That is, today we conceive of the following structures for these particular nuclei: The helium nucleus has two protons and two neutrons; the nitrogen nucleus has seven protons and seven neutrons; this particular oxygen nucleus has eight protons and nine neutrons; and the hydrogen nucleus consists of one proton.

Thus, the great event was *man-made transmutation*. Alchemy had been achieved by man.

In 1919, Rutherford returned to Cambridge University to become the head of the Cavendish Laboratory, succeeding his old professor, J. J. Thomson.

Here at Cambridge he pushed his work on transmutation, on alchemy, we might say, near that old building where the alchemists once had worked in the basement.

One could say, perhaps, that Rutherford had found the Philosopher's Stone, namely, the *alpha particle*. Soon thereafter, as we shall see, protons, neutrons, other particles, and radiation itself also were used to achieve transmutations of the elements.

Rutherford was extremely happy these days. Eileen had married the physicist Fowler, and was raising a family. At the laboratory all was going exceedingly well. Rutherford was vigorous and confident.

He was a straightforward man. He could not stand pomposity or pretense, and he had a great sense of justice. His great vigor and forceful manner caused some of his friends to refer to him as a "Tribal Leader." Some said that he had a "victorious personality."

Niels Bohr, who had spent some time working with Rutherford, used to say that Rutherford's arrival at work was as though the sun had arrived at the laboratory.

Rutherford, however, could lose his temper, on occasion, particularly when he found anyone misusing a piece of apparatus. Then, he would actually rage, "like a thundercloud," as Bohr put it.

He was always surrounded by great students and research men, by colleagues who were inspired by him and who deeply admired him. There was Chadwick, Oliphant, Cockroft, Walton, and many, many others, some of whom we have already mentioned.

In 1932, J. D. Cockcroft (1897-   ) and E. T. Walton (1903-   ) used fast, accelerated hydrogen nuclei as "bullets" to bombard various targets. They achieved more transmutation, more "alchemy," by this technique.

Here's what happened:

$$p \quad + \quad Li \quad \longrightarrow \quad \alpha \quad + \quad \alpha$$

$$_1H^1 \quad + \quad _3Li^7 \quad \longrightarrow \quad _2He^4 \quad + \quad _2He^4$$

In 1933, the husband and wife team Joliot-Curie, as you recall, discovered artificial radioactivity. This discovery is another instance of transmutation of the elements.

And today, yes, even *gold* can be produced from another material, if that is the way you want to make money, though the process is not an efficient one.

In summary, then, we can say:

1. Nature is an alchemist. It is an alchemist, for example, in changing uranium, through a series of transformations, into thorium, eventually into radium, and ultimately into

lead. Rutherford recognized this. He then became an alchemist himself, the first man to be one. In addition,

2. Rutherford discovered the nature of the radiations: α is the helium nucleus; β is a small negatively charged particle.

3. Rutherford formulated the *Theory of Radioactive Transformations*.

4. Rutherford is responsible for the *nuclear atom*.

5. Rutherford predicted the existence of the neutron.

One might also add, on the personal side, that his inspirational qualities were of a high order. He inspired scientists throughout the world.

Though he spent nearly his entire life in his work, he nevertheless found time to help those in distress. For example, he aided refugees from Germany, at a trying time in history. On his deathbed, even, he reminded his wife, "I want to leave one hundred pounds to Nelson College."

He had had a happy childhood, a happy maturity. Sir James Jeans (1877-1946), the English physicist and astronomer, said, "He was ever the happy warrior."

He was also ever the champion of science, and he once wrote, "I have become more and more impressed by the power of the scientific method of extending our knowledge of Nature."

He had done an incredible amount of original work. True, he had depended on others. He had stood on the shoulders of other giants: Becquerel, Marie and Pierre Curie, J. J. Thomson.

Others, in the future, would stand on his shoulders, and reach a little higher into our mysterious and majestic universe.

Goddard

Robert Hutchings Goddard

1882-1945

Jules Verne had written a wonderful story telling how an enormous cannon, nine hundred feet long, fired a manned capsule to the moon, and around the moon.

Robert Goddard knew that the cannon technique would never have worked. The whole thing, he could see, would have blown apart. Goddard knew that a rocket has to be used for such firings.

And here is a strange coincidence. Jules Verne in his story did use rockets for slowing the capsule down in the maneuver we nowadays call "retrorocket."

Hence, it is surprising that Verne did not use the rocket principle for the *launching* of his fictional astronauts, or cosmonauts. Verne, it is interesting to note, had his take-off base set in Florida. His base was not too far from Cape Canaveral, believe it or not.

In Russia, Konstantin Tsiolkovsky, a brilliant school teacher, also knew about the rocket principle, and he worked out the theory of propulsion and of flight before this century even began.

Then, too, we might as well mention Chinese experimenters of long, long ago. Many fireworks operate on the rocket principle, and, as you know, the Chinese invented these showy devices. There is even the story, which may be true, about the Chinese inventor who tied a bunch of rockets together, lashed himself to the whole works, and told his assistants to light the rockets so that he might be propelled to the moon.

This would-be spaceman, as everyone knows, did not turn out to be the first man on the moon. The whole kaboodle exploded, and the Chinese inventor went traveling through space in many directions at the same time—which is no way to go space traveling.

I think we had better agree on the principle of rocket propulsion before we go any further. (I get many letters from people who have unusual notions on the subject.)

Let us assume that we have a box with ignited fuel.

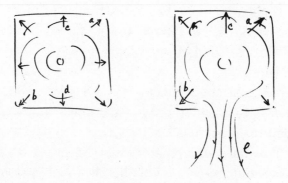

The gases press in every direction. The pressures, such as *a* and *b* cancel out. Likewise, the pressures *c* and *d* offset each other. Therefore, the box does not move unless it buckles out or explodes. It goes neither to the left nor to the right, neither up nor down.

Now, if the box has a hole in the floor, a different effect is achieved. We have action.

Pressures such as *a* and *b* still cancel out. But what about *c* and *d*? There is no pressure *d* on the box now, because the gases simply run out. They escape through the hole in the floor. Therefore, *c* presses upward on the ceiling, and lifts the box. That's it—that's the whole bit. A rocket is a box of fuel with a hole in the floor.

The total upward pressure, *c*, on the box is the "thrust." For some strange reason, many people point to the exhaust *e*, and call that the thrust. Then they talk about these emerging gases "pushing on the air outside," mistakenly assuming that "this air is resilient and sort of pushes back upward on the rocket!"

In reality, the thrust on the rocket is at *c*. And even if we have no air outside for *e* to push on, as in a vacuum, the rocket still goes. It makes no difference. The thrust is at *c*, and the rocket goes, unless it happens to be too heavy.

A German, Hermann Oberth (1894-   ), worked brilliantly on the design of rockets. He also brought forth many ideas on the theory of space flight.

Another rocket pioneer was an American, Robert Hutchings Goddard. Goddard, a college professor and a man of unusual intelligence, was one of the first in our times not only to believe in space flight but to do something about it.

But don't assume that Goddard was "the toast of the town" because of his pioneering rocket experiments. Let me, in fact, put it this way. He was driven out of town. Goddard lived in a community in one of the New England states, and the fine citizens thought he was nuts for firing those objects in the forests.

"What if he starts a fire?" some asked. "Maybe he'll even burn us out of our homes."

"And he's noisy and a nuisance," others chimed in. "He's different!"

Accordingly, they reported him to the fire marshall.

A bitter and sullen Robert Goddard, for some unique reason, left his native state, heading for New Mexico. Anyway, the New England winters were unsuitable for rocket work.

I recall writing a letter to Goddard at about this time in the '30's, asking if I could come out to New Mexico and help with the work. However, affairs took a different turn, and I went in another direction (to Panama).

As far back as 1916, Goddard had made a study, which three years later was published as a scientific paper about seventy pages long, entitled *A Method of Reaching Extreme Altitudes*.

Goddard even spoke of hitting the moon, and of having a flash powder explode on contact in order that we might see the hit from Earth.

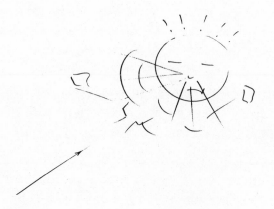

In the 1930's Goddard was using liquid fuels, and he worked on such early refinements as stabilization by gyroscope, and change in direction by having the exhaust glance off a vane in its path.

What will happen in such a case? Can you tell?

To improve the performance of his rockets, he made them stronger and more able to withstand higher gas pressures, and he fashioned a tapered exhaust nozzle—much copied today—to give smoother and more continuous flow.

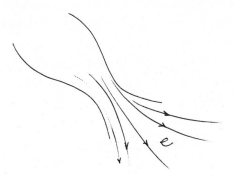

At the time of World War I, Goddard had received some government funds to develop long-range rockets for military use. At that time, he had used a powder propellant, 40 per cent nitroglycerine and 60 per cent nitrocellulose.

(I do not advise young rocketeers to experiment with fuels. Even mature experts have all they can do to prevent slight misjudgments. Three rocket-fuel engineers were blown to bits the other day. Young rocketeers should study rocket theory and instrumentation. Above all, if they really want to become space engineers or space scientists, they must study *mathematics.*)

Goddard's solid-fuel rockets of those days were fired from launchers held in the hands!

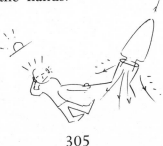

These rockets ranged in weight from about 1.5 pounds to 17 pounds.

He fashioned also designs of four-inch rockets to be fired from airplanes. And, of course, today we have all kinds of rockets which are dispatched by airplanes.

In peacetime, Robert Goddard pursued his high-altitude research, which was his real interest. He switched to the use of a liquid propellant. He used gasoline and liquid oxygen.

Some people have the misconception that liquid oxygen is a fuel. When they observe our enormous rocket boosters being readied, they may remark on the white billowing "fuel" that is bubbling over. The oxygen, in reality, is the *oxidizer*. The fuel is gasoline, which requires the oxygen in order to produce burning.

The oxygen is used in liquid form simply because the liquid is more compact than gaseous oxygen. The billowing is the inevitable evaporation of a small amount of the very cold liquid oxygen.

Oxygen and the actual fuel together are called the "propellant." It cannot be denied that loading up with liquid propellant, particularly the liquid oxygen, is a nuisance and an inordinate waste of time. We may be certain that solid-fuel rockets will receive more attention through the years.

Some of Robert Goddard's designs were used by the Germans in World War II in their famous (or infamous?) *V-2* missiles. The *V-2* burned a liquid propellant—a mixture of liquid oxygen and alcohol. Goddard had proposed rockets such as the *V-2* during the years 1914-1940, but one man can't build such a device by himself, and apparently nobody paid any attention to him.

The designation *V-2* stood for "Vergeltungswaffe Zwei"— "Revenge Weapon No. 2." Churchill, as you may recall, took the *V* and made it a sign for "Victory." One might ponder whether or not Victory with justice is mightier than Revenge. Especially revenge for what?

The *V-2* was 46 feet long, and 5.5 feet in diameter. It weighed 13 tons fully loaded. Its rocket engine used 7,600 pounds of alcohol and 11,000 pounds of liquid oxygen, all to deliver an explosive "payload," or warhead, of about 2,100 pounds.

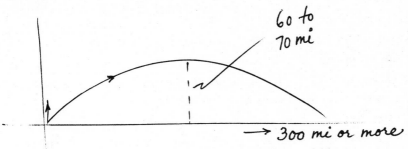

The *V-2's* rose vertically, then tilted, and were off!

They burned up their propellant in the first 65 seconds, and had a thrust of about 68,000 pounds, which is about the same as that of the United States Redstone.

One of the terror-inspiring features of the *V-2* was that it traveled faster than sound, and thus gave the warning noise of the flight only after it had hit the target and dealt its death blow.

The *V-1* was essentially an unmanned flying airplane, jet propelled. It was much slower than the rocket *V-2*. Many *V-1*'s were shot down by pursuing planes. Not so the *V-2*'s.

We should mention that several years before World War II not only the Germans but also the Russians and the English began to develop rocket weapons. The Russians, having the rocket tradition of Konstantin Tsiolkovsky behind them, were particularly successful in developing a truck-portable mass array of rockets, "Katusha"—"Oh you, Kate"—which decimated the Nazis as they pressed deep into Russia.

Robert Goddard was an excellent mathematician, as well as a research physicist. He had been the head of the physics department at Clark University, and he knew all the rocket theory. It was no trouble at all for him to calculate the velocity that a rocket should acquire. Would you care to have the standard theoretical formula?

$$V = V_o + V_e \times ln\left(\frac{M_o}{M}\right)$$

Here V is the velocity the rocket will finally acquire; V_o is its original velocity—for example, if it is launched from an airplane before its own propellant goes to work; V_e is the velocity of the exhaust material; M_o is the total mass of the rocket and fuel at the start; M is the final traveling mass, or payload mass; ln means the natural logarithm.

In any case, you can see that a rocket's final velocity V depends on the exhaust velocity and on the *ratio* of the total starting mass to the final mass.

Goddard knew that it is difficult to get a large $\frac{M_o}{M}$ (mass ratio) in a one-step rocket. Yet, it is not so difficult to achieve this big "mass ratio" if one uses the "step principle," or the multiple "piggy-back" system. One obvious advantage: casings are discarded one by one; why waste fuel accelerating the empty shells? A one-stage rocket of the same weight would carry the empty shell.

Rocket A carries all the rest until it achieves maximum speed, then B, carrying the others, fires; after it has reached maximum speed, C, carrying the others, fires; and so it goes until E streaks away from earth to Mars. Goddard, and others, too, promoted the piggy-back technique, and, now, we use it.

World War II saw Robert Goddard at work with rockets at Annapolis. By the end of the war, the United States was producing rockets at the incredible rate of one billion per year. Most of these rockets, of course, were artillery types—not the giants now seen on the launching pads. Not all the credit for this production should go to Goddard, but we must admit that he had been and was in there pitching, all his life.

One thousand eight hundred years ago, Lukian of Samosata taught that the earth's atmosphere enveloped the moon, and that a powerful storm in the Atlantic Ocean could blow a sailing vessel to the moon.

"It would take seven days," he calculated, "and the landing will be on the eighth, upon the moon—which is like a shining island."

This vision has come true. There are launching "storms" near the oceans, whence ships rise to travel to the moon in even less than seven days. And the times have come for trips to the planets, too. And the trip actually can be made on the solar wind! Pressed by the rays of the sun, spaceships can make interplanetary flights.

Ancient prophets are forever reborn; in all ages, it seems, they are ignored and even driven from their tramping grounds.

On August 10, 1945, after a throat operation, Robert Hutchings Goddard died. We now have a great space research center named for him—the Goddard Space Flight Center, Greenbelt, Md. What he really needed was some co-operation and consideration at the time the magical vision of space flight loomed before his gaze.

Fermi

24

Enrico Fermi

1901-1954

On December 2, 1942, so goes the story, Professor Arthur Compton put in a long-distance call to Dr. James Conant.

"The Italian navigator," reported Compton, trying to control his excitement, " . . . the Italian navigator has reached the New World."

"And how," replied Conant, " . . . how did he find the natives?"

"Very friendly."

Enrico Fermi had certainly reached a New World. He had produced the first chain reaction, in a nuclear pile at the University of Chicago.

Later, at a house party, the excitement among Fermi's crew of scientists kept bubbling over. Fermi's wife, Laura, tried to divine what had occurred. But the scientists had been sworn to secrecy.

A young scientist, Leona Woods, merrily chirped to Laura, "Enrico has sunk a Japanese admiral."

Not long afterward, the Japanese people themselves were to feel the effects of this nuclear discovery. But, at the time of the house party, the reaction was not yet a bomb. It was a controlled reaction, and it went like this:

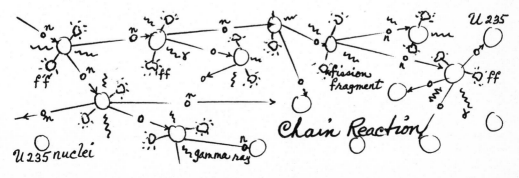

This chain reaction opened up an entire world of new possibilities and achievements. There were bombs, of course, of a number of varieties. There followed, too, reactors of many types for various purposes. Eventually, there came a profusion of radioactive substances produced artificially, many of great value for peaceful purposes.

A new Columbus had attained a New World. And we have as yet barely touched upon its superabounding shores. Atomic energy will become more important year by year.

Enrico Fermi was born in Rome. He received a Doctor of Philosophy degree from the University of Pisa, where, you recall, Galileo had once leaned out of the tower. Fermi became lecturer at the University of Florence, later going to the University of Rome as a professor.

In 1934, Fermi, contemplating the new particles, *neutrons,* which Chadwick of England had recently discovered, had an idea. It was this:

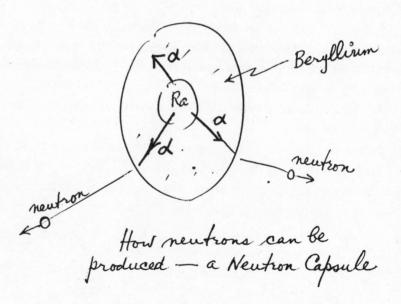

How neutrons can be produced — a Neutron Capsule

Since neutrons have no electrical charge, they should be able to penetrate the nucleus of an atom without any oppo-

sition. Perhaps they could bring about nuclear changes. Maybe they could dislodge protons, and thus create a new
element.

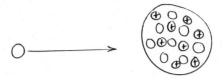

A proton, with its positive charge is repelled when fired
into a nucleus. It can, of course, enter the nucleus if it is
fired at excessive speeds. Neutrons, on the other hand, would
have a much easier time in getting into the nucleus.

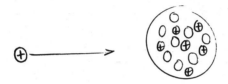

It worked. Fermi showed that nuclear transformations take
place in nearly all elements which are bombarded by neutrons.
Here, for example, are some "alchemies" that can occur:

1. Neutrons hit lithium-6. This produces *triton* (a very
heavy hydrogen nucleus) and a helium nucleus (or alpha
particle).

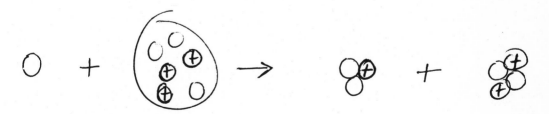

This can all be written as:

$$_0n^1 + {_3}Li^6 \rightarrow {_1}H^3 + {_2}He^4$$

313

2. Neutrons bombard boron-10 to produce lithium-7 and helium:

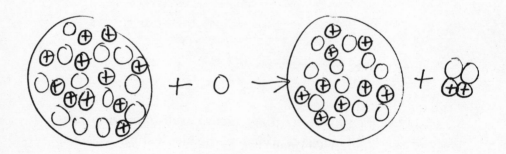

$$_0n^1 + {}_5B^{10} \rightarrow {}_3Li^7 + {}_2He^4$$

3. Neutrons bombard sodium-23, giving fluorine-20 and an alpha particle:

$$_0n^1 + {}_{11}Na^{23} \rightarrow {}_9F^{20} + {}_2He^4$$

In such reactions, the new nucleus might be radioactive and go on to emit particles from itself. Do you recall that Marie Curie's daughter, Irene, discovered artificial radioactivity?

Fermi was occupied in 1934 with letting neutrons fly at all sorts of targets, and observing what came out! Thus, he could tell how the elements were being changed, or transmuted.

The Fermi family pulled a fast one on Mussolini. The Fermis wanted to get out of Italy because Laura, being Jewish, felt uneasy in the undemocratic regime.

In 1938, Enrico received the Nobel prize in physics for his work on artificially radioactive substances. Accordingly, when the time came for him to accept the award in Sweden, the family, after secretly making arrangements regarding their various possessions, set off for Sweden. There, Enrico Fermi accepted the prize, and the family kept on going directly to the United States.

How fortunate we were! As you know, in the United States Fermi made the chain reaction work. This attainment soon led to the development of the controlled release of atomic energy, whether in modest flow or in great bursts.

In this country, Fermi went first to Columbia University, in 1939, then to the University of Chicago. Later, he moved to Los Alamos to work on the atomic bomb. Then, in 1945, he returned to Chicago as Professor at the Institute for Nuclear Studies.

Fermi's escape from Italy reminds one that Hitler, too, lost out scientifically because of race prejudice. The gentle and brilliant Jewish woman, Lise Meitner (1878-   ), had been in on the discovery of the fission of uranium. Fearing for her life, she left Germany for Stockholm, while there was yet a chance to escape from the Nazis. In Sweden, Lise learned about the startling work of Otto Hahn (1879-   ) and Fritz Strassman (1901-   ) on uranium.

Lise Meitner went to Copenhagen, where she made calculations with her nephew, the physicist Otto Frisch, who was also a refugee from Hitler. Lise and Otto figured out the meaning of the uranium experiments. They saw that uranium nuclei could be split, releasing a tremendous amount of energy along with more neutrons, which could repeat the process, thus giving a chain reaction.

Lise and Otto sought out the great Danish physicist Niels Bohr, and it was decided that Bohr would go to the United States, if he could. The Danish waters were patrolled by Nazi boats.

The Danish underground went to work. Underground agents arranged a rendezvous with a British warship. Accordingly, one dark night, a burly, blond man stole out to sea in a small boat. Nazi searchlights almost spotted the boat. But Niels Bohr slipped through the waters, and a friendly ship picked him up. Bohr, who became "Mr. Baker," came to the United States with the great calculations about uranium in his head.

There were meetings with Einstein, another refugee from the Nazis. In July 1939, the scientists Leo Szilard (1898-) and Eugene Wigner (1902-) also visited Einstein, informing him that the fission of uranium was a fact, having been checked out at Columbia University.

On August 2, 1939, Einstein wrote a letter to President Franklin D. Roosevelt, telling the president of the possibility of creating a superbomb through atomic energy. Einstein suggested that the United States get started on such a project immediately in order to beat the Nazis to the punch. President Roosevelt set the *Manhattan Project* in operation. And Enrico Fermi made the chain go. Then came the Bombs.

Incidentally, before Bohr left Denmark, he dissolved his golden Nobel prize in a bottle of acid, and left the bottle standing on a shelf. It remained there throughout the war, in Copenhagen, under Nazi eyes, to mock them silently. After the war, Bohr found the bottle, precipitated the gold, and recast his Nobel medal.

Enrico Fermi, meanwhile, found that slow neutrons can break up uranium-235 more effectively than fast neutrons. The slow neutrons spend more time in the vicinity of the nucleus than the fast ones. Thus, the slow neutrons can exert a greater effect on the nucleus.

The process is somewhat similar to the sun's working on a passing comet. If the comet moves slowly, the sun has more time to pull on it, and will disrupt it more than if the comet had merely whizzed past.

Accordingly, a *moderator* consisting of carbon blocks (graphite) or heavy water is used in atomic reactors. The carbon blocks or heavy water slow down, or moderate, the neutrons.

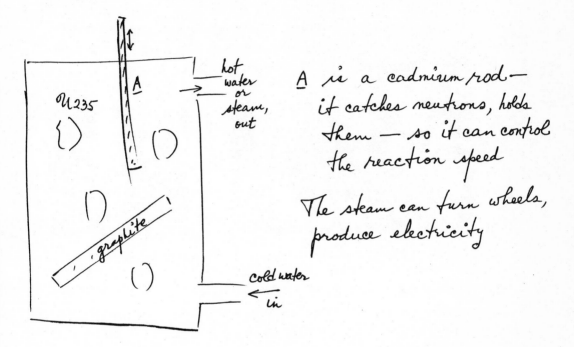

U_{235}

graphite

hot water or steam, out

cold water in

A is a cadmium rod — it catches neutrons, holds them — so it can control the reaction speed

The steam can turn wheels, produce electricity

While a chain runs, we can put in various substances, such as phosphorus or containers of iodine, and they all will become radioactive in the neutron cross fire. Afterwards, these radioactive *isotopes* can be used in research or in medical treatment of cancer.

I used to work with some of these radioactive substances. Here are some of the experiments:

For example, I gave a hen an injection in the shoulder of
radioactive phosphorus solution. The hen laid radioactive
eggs for three weeks. When I hard-boiled the eggs and tried
out the various parts on the Geiger counter, I found that the
radioactivity was mostly in the shell.

Then I gave a pregnant laboratory animal an injection of
radioactive phosphorus in the back of the neck. Ten young
ones, born four days later, were all radioactive.

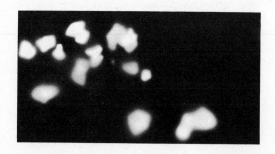 

Suppose we have some uranium-238 along with uranium-
235. A very important event then occurs. The U^{238} atoms
capture some of the neutrons from the radioactive uranium-
235. Uranium-238 becomes uranium-239 (another isotope of
uranium).

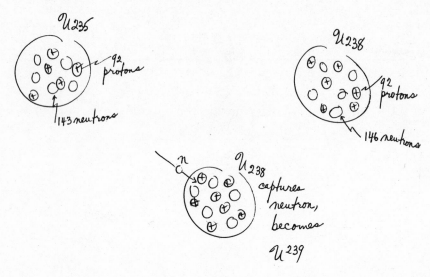

Uranium-239 is highly radioactive. It emits an electron (a beta particle) from its nucleus. The electron comes from a neutron! The neutron then becomes a proton. The nucleus now has ninety-three protons. The original uranium atom has changed into a new element. We call this element *neptunium*.

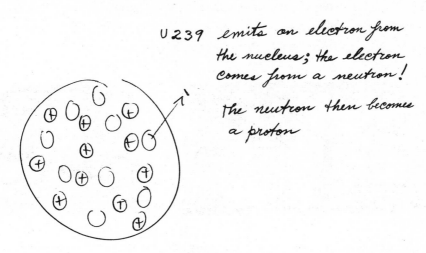

U 239 emits an electron from the nucleus; the electron comes from a neutron!

The neutron then becomes a proton

Neptunium is an unstable element. It soon emits an electron from its nucleus. With the emission of the electron, neptunium changes to a nucleus having ninety-four protons. Again, we have another element. This one is called *plutonium*.

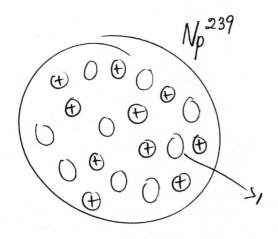

Np²³⁹

Neutron becomes a proton

Now, what's the point? The point is that the *plutonium is fissionable*. It can be used for a controlled chain reaction, or, for an uncontrolled one—the Bomb.

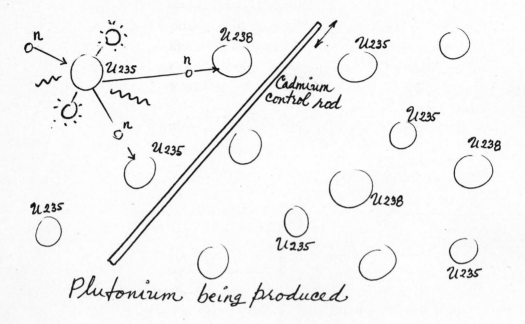

Plutonium being produced

The chain reaction from plutonium goes like this:

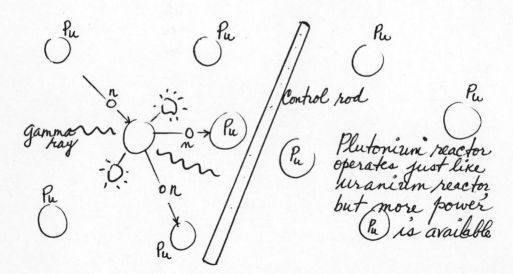

Incidentally, if the plutonium pieces are very close together, the chain becomes almost instantaneous, and we get
a plutonium A-bomb. Similar remarks apply to uranium-235.

The atomic bomb first brought atomic energy and its significance to the attention of people all over the world. Now,
fortunately, we are giving a great deal of attention to peaceful applications of atomic energy. Big reactors, we have seen,
can be used successfully to turn the generators in electric-
power plants.

The design for a reactor built in England is sketched below:

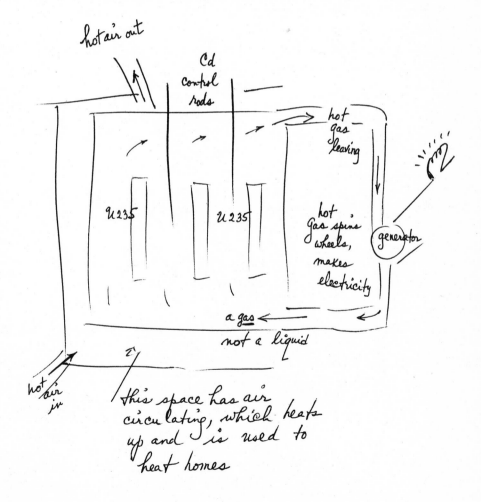

Even more awesome than the uranium bomb, as we all know, is the hydrogen bomb, or H-bomb. An ordinary U-bomb is used to trigger the hydrogen bomb. The enormous heat the U-bomb trigger produces causes deuterons in the H-bomb to *fuse,* or come together:

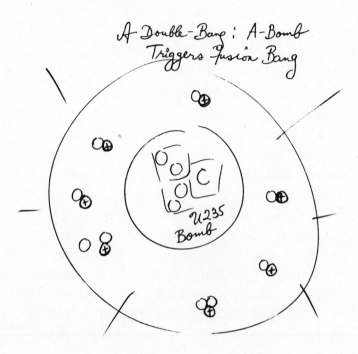

In fusing, the deuterons lose some of their mass, and this lost mass becomes an enormous amount of energy.

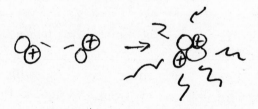

The process in which particles come together, stick, and emit energy is called *fusion.* Fusion is constantly going on in the sun. The sun gets its energy by fusing hydrogen into helium, though it does this in a round-about way, not by a direct process.

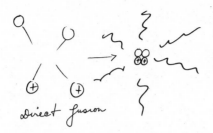

Direct fusion

In fusion, as we have seen, the mass becomes energy according to Einstein's formula $E = mc^2$, where m is the lost mass, c is the velocity of light, and E is the energy produced. The velocity of light, you recall, is 186,000 miles per second. You can see that the loss of only a small bit of matter produces an extraordinary amount of energy.

Enrico Fermi was an excellent teacher, as well as one of the greatest of physicists. He was a learned man in general, and a man who loved life. In his youth, he was a great hiker. He was, as his wife Laura has said, "A tall, strong physicist." She tells a great deal about him in her books, one of which is entitled *Atoms in the Family: My Life with Enrico Fermi.*[1]

He was a navigator who landed in a most startling and exciting world—the world of atomic energy with its promise of greatness for planetary inhabitants who can measure up to greatness.

But Enrico Fermi did not remain long to see how his New World would make out.

In 1954, he died of cancer—a disease which sometimes can be cured by his energy from the atoms. But, for him, the discovery of the illness came too late.

---

[1]Laura Fermi, *Atoms in the Family: My Life with Enrico Fermi* (Chicago: The University of Chicago Press, 1954).

Hubble

MT. WILSON AND PALOMAR OBSERVATORIES

25

Edwin Powell Hubble

1889-1953

A long time ago a scholar named Bruno said, "There are multitudes of other worlds in space—worlds like our own on earth. They surround other suns, and have beings. . . ."

Giordano Bruno (*fl* 1548-1600) was burned at the stake for his vision. There were people who did not like his ideas.

The astronomer Halley, friend of Isaac Newton, discovered and listed six patches in the constellation Hercules. Were these even more distant world systems than the mere individual suns of which Bruno spoke?

The brother-sister team of William and Caroline Herschel, and William's son, John, after him, observed more than 5,000 "nebulae!" What were these patches of light—circular, elliptical, and irregular-shaped?

Thomas Wright, an amateur astronomer, speculated in the eighteenth century that the stars are like the sun, and that their distances could be estimated by their degree of brightness or faintness. Wright thought even of a star system beyond our Milky Way. He reasoned that one single star system, alone in the universe, was too poor an undertaking for nature.

Wright said, "I can imagine other similar vast systems of stars. And we have evidence. Consider the mysterious clouds called 'nebulae.' "

A few years later the philosopher Immanuel Kant (1724-1804) elaborated upon Wright's ideas, and Kant's conception remained of permanent value:

Let us imagine a system of stars, all together in a common plane, such as is the case with the Milky Way, but located so far away from us that even with telescope we cannot distinguish the individual stars composing it. . . . such a world of stars will appear to the observer who studies it at such an enormous distance only as a small spot feebly illumined. . . . its shape will be circular, if its plane is perpendicular to the line of sight, elliptical, if it is seen at an angle. The faintness of its light, its form, and its considerable diameter will clearly distinguish such a phenomenon from the isolated stars around it.

It all came true. All so true.

And one of the Earth people most responsible for really making it completely clear that Our Galaxy is one among countless others was Edwin Hubble.

A graduate of the University of Chicago, a Rhodes scholar, Hubble went to work for several years at the Yerkes Observatory, then moved on to the Mount Wilson Observatory, where he became the director.

Hubble threw himself into the study of the heavens with all his being. There was nothing he neglected—neither the individual stars nor the nebulae.

The nebulae. He turned the best telescope in the world on them, and he photographed them on every night of good "seeing." The photographic method, you realize, is far superior to the visual method. Why? When you look through a telescope, the eye becomes tired, and you see less. If, however, you use a camera on long-time exposure, the light keeps building up. Invisible bodies appear on the negative.

Hubble found worlds and worlds and worlds. The nebulous nebulae were galaxies, Island Universes in space.

At times, Hubble carried out his observations from Mount Palomar Observatory, which is associated with the Mount Wilson Observatory.

The Mount Palomar telescope can reach about one trillion galaxies. And each galaxy has perhaps from thirty billion to more than two hundred billion stars, or suns. And how many of these suns have Good (or habitable) Earths?

Hubble, with many other accomplished astronomers, worked for a lifetime on the magnificent Island Universes, measuring their brightness, their distance, their distribution.

One of the greatest of the astronomers in this exploration of the universe was Harlow Shapley (1885-   ) of Harvard. Shapley, too, worked at Mount Palomar, from 1914 to 1921. He was director of the Harvard Observatory from 1921 to 1952.

There were many others who opened up the heavens for us all. I have a feeling that if we do not know of the universe about us—its majesty, its extent, its galaxies without end— then we cannot know ourselves.

Immanual Kant had written, "There are two things which fill me with eternal wonder—the starry sky above us, and the moral law within us."

Then Hubble, with other astronomers, found an amazing thing: the galaxies are running away from each other!

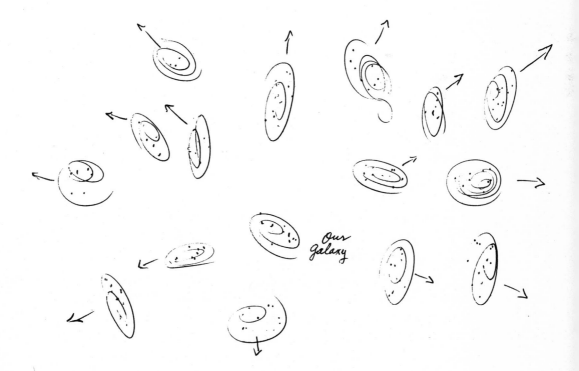

Our
galaxy

They seem to be running away from *us*. Yet, it is easy to understand that an astronomer on another galaxy would say, "They are running away from us." Can everyone say such a thing, no matter on which galaxy? Yes. How about thinking of it all this way: We have a balloon with spots—galaxies— on it. The balloon is being inflated.

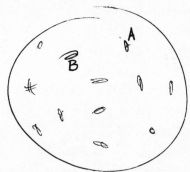

If we stand at *A*, as the balloon inflates, every "galaxy" will be running away from us. Yet, when we stand at *B*, we'll say the same thing. Every galaxy still runs away.

The universe is expanding, astronomers concluded. What a remarkable conclusion.

There was a *theory* about a universe that could be expanding, and here Hubble was bringing in the observational facts.

Before I forget, I want to say that not every galaxy runs away from every other. Here is what I mean:

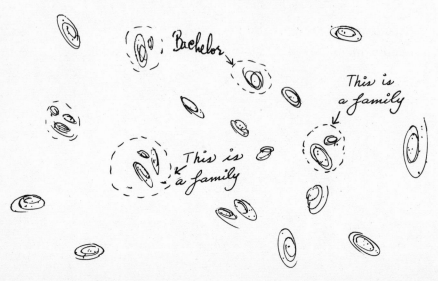

Whole *families* of galaxies run away from each other. But members of an individual family usually approach each other, because of mutual gravitational attraction.

We still, then, have an expanding universe.

Incidentally, some of the galaxies have collided. They were probably members of a family who met for a reunion.

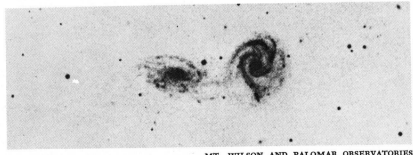

Galaxies in collision

MT. WILSON AND PALOMAR OBSERVATORIES

Possibly the colliding galaxies, however, according to a Russian astronomer, are really *one* galaxy that is breaking apart.

The colliding galaxies send out enormous amounts of radio energy, which we pick up with our radio telescopes. One pair in its collision generates so much energy that, if we could catch all the emitted energy for one second, it would suffice to run all the works of man on earth for one trillion years.

What do you suppose is happening on some of those Good Earths of some of those suns which make up those colliding galaxies? Actually, stars, or suns, are generally so far apart that they may only rarely collide in the collision of their galaxies. The emitted energy must come from the collision of the sparse gases between the stars, and from the gravitational twistings produced by the interpenetrating systems.

Yet, why are the galaxies running away from each other? This we do not know. Of course, there are theories. Perhaps Abbe Lemaitre, the Belgian priest-scientist, was right. He supposed that once upon a time all the energy and matter of the universe were contained in one compact enormous "atom," perhaps some ten million miles in diameter. This huge atom was extremely hot, or radioactive, and exploded!

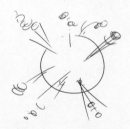

The pieces became galaxies, traveling outward. It is a good theory, and has been holding its own for a long time.

Hubble found that the more distant galaxies run away faster than those closer to us. How come? Let's think of the expanding balloon again.

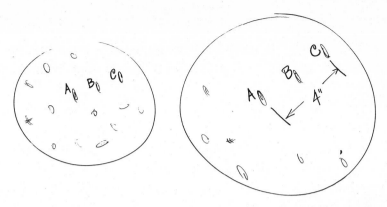

Let us say that *AB* is one inch and *AC* is two inches. Now, let the balloon expand in one second so that *AB* is two inches. How much will *AC* be?

AC will be four inches. The more distant *C*, you see, is running away at two inches per second, while *B* is moving away at only one inch per second. Right?

So it is with galaxies.

But, let's face it, how do we really know that the galaxies are running away, say from us?

Remember what happens when a train whistle is approaching you? The pitch seems shrill. And, when the train is running away from you, the pitch seems lower than when the train is at rest. So it is with *light* from the galaxies.

First, let's work with light produced on earth. Pick out one glowing substance, hydrogen. It emits a number of colors. Let's take one color.

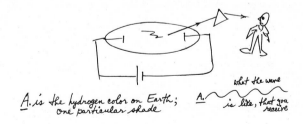

A. is the hydrogen color on Earth; one particular shade   A. what the wave is like, that you receive

Now, find the glowing hydrogen of some distant galaxy, and study the color.

The wave length of the hydrogen emission from the galaxy is longer than from that on earth. The color is more *reddish*. Yellow colors are orange-ish, orange ones are reddish, and red ones are more red. This action is like the lowering of the pitch from the receding train whistle.

From the amount of "red shift" Hubble could calculate how far away the galaxies were. (Remember the balloon?) The more distant galaxies move away faster than the close ones. Some galaxies run away from us at 10,000 miles per second, others at 40,000 miles per second!

What is the fastest possible? Then what? We can think of a galaxy which is moving away so fast—or, space is expanding so fast at the position of that galaxy—that its light will never reach us. That would be that. We could never know of the universe beyond those limits?

How far away are the farthest galaxies?

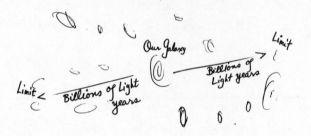

This of course means that the light from those distant galaxies has been traveling toward us for billions of years and has only now arrived. Then those galaxies certainly are not "now" where we see them. Haven't they been traveling away while the light has been coming at us? And, by the way, perhaps some of those we see do not exist now at all! Maybe some have exploded or have died out in the several billion years since their images have started toward us.

Have you ever thought about this? *Everything* we see is back in time. A view of the moon is about 1-1/3 seconds into the past; a view of the sun is more than eight minutes in the past; a view of the Planet Pluto is about six hours in the past; a view of a star may be millions of years old; and the galactic images in our heads are millions or billions of years into the past. Talk about looking back in time! We actually always do.

There is one important thing that we have not touched on: How do you get the *distance* of a galaxy from us? After all, the change in color can only tell us how *fast* a galaxy is moving away, and that another may be moving away twice as fast and is therefore twice as far away. Twice as far as *how much*? We *must* get the distance of one galaxy, at least.

In 1912, at Harvard, Henrietta Levitt had discovered a startling fact. Certain stars are variable in a periodic way, their light growing stronger, then weaker, then repeating again, with a regular time beat!

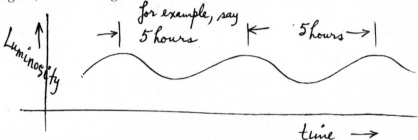

The amazing thing was that there were *many* which had, say, a five-hour period; there were many also which had, say, an eight-hour period; many which had, say, a twelve-day period; and so on. These variables came in families.

Each family, it became evident, consisted of almost identical stars.

Now, let us see what this all can mean.

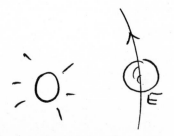

Let us assume that we can determine the distance of Star *A* from earth by the base-line method.

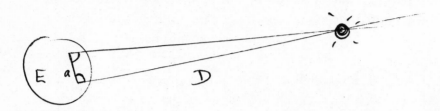

We know *a* and two angles, so it is easy to get *D*.

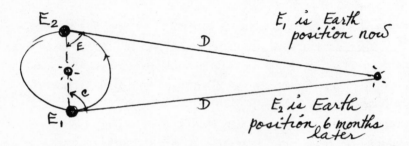

Or, if the star is far, far away we measure the angles *C* and *E*, and we know that the base line is 186,000,000 miles, so we can easily get *D*.

Now assume that *B*, one of those variable stars, is near the star *A*. (The first variable star discovered was in the constellation of Cepheus, so let's call such stars Cepheid Variable, or a Cepheid.) Accordingly, we measure the distance of *B* by the base-line method. We record its light curve.

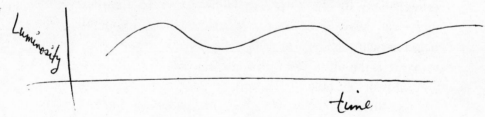

Now, we look for the same type of star—same family, same period—in some other galaxy than our own. Hubble found one of these stars! He was the first astronomer to observe a Cepheid variable in a galaxy beyond ours. He could detect its change in light, and he could time its period.

What did he do next?

He plotted its light curve.

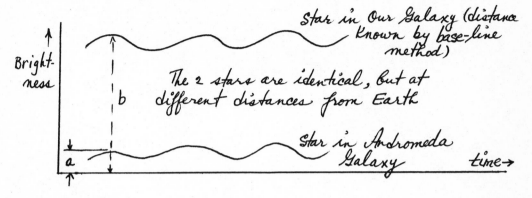

Suppose that *a* is one million times weaker than *b*. We can measure its intensity with photoelectric cells. From our knowledge of how light spreads out spherically (area of a sphere depends on R^2, hence the light must thin out over the sphere, and it decreases in strength correspondingly), we conclude that the other-galaxy star is one thousand times farther away from us than the near star, whose distance we have measured. Now we have *miles,* or *light years.* Now we are in business. We next measure the change in wave length from this galaxy whose distance we know, and this gives us *speed* and *distance.* If we measure the speed now of any other galaxy by the wave-length change method, we immediately can give the *distance* of the galaxy. Remember the balloon again? The faster a galaxy runs away, the farther away it is from us, in direct proportion.

Professor Hubble photographed our universe for us, and he measured it, also. He died unexpectedly in 1953. Astronomers will say he did not die. He lives through his work, and in the distances of space, and in the magical reaches of the Expanding Universe.

Einstein

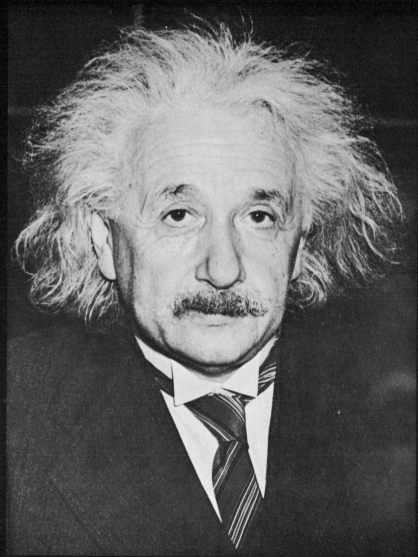

Albert Einstein

1879-1955

Professor Einstein explained many things about the tiny atoms and small bits of energy. He also explained many things about the immense universe and the great forces which act in it. And the important thing is that he did it all with the rigorous logic of mathematics.

One of the tiny effects which he explained mathematically was the meaning of the photoelectric effect. You remember that Heinrich Hertz was the first to notice that ultraviolet light which fell upon one of his spark gaps helped the spark to take place, but Hertz did not realize what exactly was the cause of this interesting behavior. Einstein showed that "packets" of light, or "quanta" of light, fall upon the negative plate and kick out electrons.

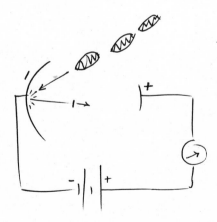

The electrons are then pulled over by the positive plate, and we have a complete circuit, with the instrument indicating that current is passing.

Einstein worked out the equation connecting the color of the light—or, its wave length or frequency—with the speed which the ejected electrons will have. He showed that each quantum of light makes the surface emit one electron, and that the shorter the wave length of the light making up the quantum, the more energy will the ejected electron have.

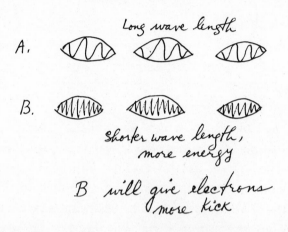

A. Long wave length

B. Shorter wave length, more energy

B will give electrons more kick

Einstein also explained something called *Brownian motion*. If we have some very light material in small—very tiny—pieces suspended in water, we can see these tiny bits of matter jiggle around.

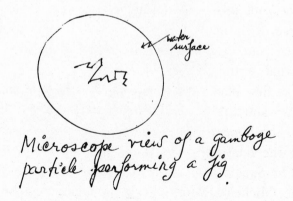

water surface

Microscope view of a gamboge particle performing a jig.

Professor Einstein showed that this jiggling was due to the bombardment of the bit of matter by the molecules of water.

He worked out the precise relation connecting all the factors, such as mass of particle, temperature of the water, distance moved. . . .

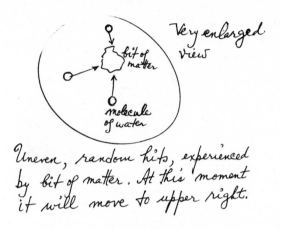

Uneven, random hits, experienced by bit of matter. At this moment it will move to upper right.

But everyone knows that Einstein's really great work was in producing the *Theory of Relativity*. And I think that I had better hurry up and tell what the *Theory of Relativity* is *not*. It is not a statement that "everything is relative." It is not a statement that "a mountain is large compared with a man, but a mountain is small compared with a planet, and a man is large compared with a germ. . . ."

It does not take a genius to tell us that a planet is large compared with man. In fact, only a nitwit would make a "big deal" out of things which are so obvious.

So what is the *Theory of Relativity?*

In the first place, it has two parts—the *Special Theory of Relativity* and the *General Theory of Relativity*. In addition, there is the *Unified Field Theory*, which may be regarded as part of the relativity work. Let's take them up, one by one.

1. *The Special Theory of Relativity.* First, do you remember the Michelson-Morley experiment which we discussed earlier? It was an attempt to find the absolute value of the earth's motion in space—motion relative to the assumed "ether." This ether was the something which made possible

the wave-spreading or travel of light, as water makes possible the wave-spreading or travel of ripples, or water waves.

But the Michelson-Morley experiment was "negative." They could not detect earth's "absolute" motion.

From this, Einstein concluded that the velocity of light does not depend on the velocity of the observer. And he also concluded that the velocity of light is not any different if the lamp emitting the light is coming at us or going away from us. We always get—in a vacuum or in air—about 186,000 miles per second, or 30,000,000,000 centimeters per second.

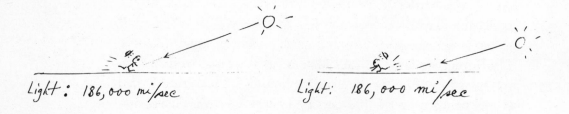

Light: 186,000 mi/sec   Light: 186,000 mi/sec

So, in 1905, Einstein said, "What do we have? Let's put together what we know of motion."

a) The velocity of light is constant.

b) Physics experiments will give the same type of results no matter in what place in the universe we perform them, so long as these places are moving with constant velocity with respect to each other. For example, experiments performed on a train moving at constant speed in a straight line are exactly like those performed on earth. In fact, you wouldn't even know that you were on a train if the shades were drawn and the inside were made to look like a home. The earth is such a train! And that's why you can't determine its "real" velocity through space, its "absolute" velocity. . . .

c) Two velocities are added by us directly. That is, (1) if a man is on a train which is traveling at 50 mph relative to the ground and (2) the man runs to the dining car at

15 mph relative to his seat, then, (3) to a person on the ground, the man is moving at 50 + 15, or 65 mph.

But Einstein saw that these three statements could not all be true. They contain a contradiction. The first and the third simply do not go together. Einstein decided that two velocities *do not* add directly, although for thousands of years we have been adding them that way. He said we haven't noticed that No. 3 was wrong, because the mistakes in using it are not noticeable until we use very big velocities—velocities nearly as big as the speed of light. Thus, the true formula for getting that hungry man's velocity with respect to the ground gives 64.99999999999999 . . . mph, and we think it's 65. *But,* if the train were a fleeting spaceship, and the man were *really* hungry and so running inside like mad, we wouldn't get the right answer by straight addition.

Einstein kept statements No. 1 and No. 2, and rejected the third. He then worked out the formula for the man's velocity relative to earth. Would you like to have it? Okay— for train, spaceship, anything

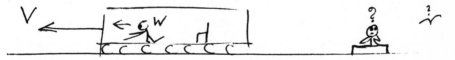

If the train has a velocity V relative to the man on the ground; and if the man has a velocity W relative to his seat, or relative to the train (right?); then, the velocity U of the man relative to the ground is given by

$$U = \frac{V + W}{1 + \dfrac{V \times W}{c^2}}$$

Here c is the velocity of light. Now, let's try this out. Take the first case that we had

$$U = \frac{50 + 15}{1 + \dfrac{50 \times 15}{(186,000 \times 60 \times 60)^2}}$$

where I had to put the c in miles per hour.

What answer do we get? It is certainly 64.999999999999 . . . mph, and we might as well say 65.

But, try this, now: Let V be fifty per cent of the speed of light, and let W also be that much. Then,

$$U = \frac{.5c + .5c}{1 + \dfrac{.5c \times .5c}{c^2}}$$

This gives

$$U = \frac{c}{1 + .25},$$

or

$$U = \frac{c}{1.25}, \text{ or } .8c$$

and not c, as we would "normally" expect from adding V, and $W = .5c$.

Now try even this: let $V = c$ and $W = c$.

$$U = \frac{c + c}{1 + \dfrac{c \times c}{c^2}}$$

or $U = c$, and not $2c$.

Thus, among other things, Einstein was showing us that the velocity of light is a *limiting* velocity. Actually, no *thing* can travel with the speed of light, and certainly things cannot travel faster than the speed of light. I am often asked, "What if a person *could* travel with a speed greater than light, would he go back in time?"

Here are some more results of Einstein's *Special Theory of Relativity*:

If an object travels relative to you, its length, as measured by you, will come out *less* than when it is at rest relative to you.

If you want the formula, here it is

$$L_2 = L_1 \sqrt{1 - \frac{v^2}{c^2}}$$

And *time* "shrinks," too. If a spaceship leaves earth and travels very fast, time on the spaceship will run more slowly than on earth.

$$T_2 = T_1 \sqrt{1 - \frac{v^2}{c^2}}$$

If the traveler goes very fast, very long, he'll come back much younger than his twin brother who remained on earth. In fact, if a grandfather goes, he could come back younger than his grandson.

Another result is this: If an object travels fast relative to you, you'll find that its mass is greater than when the object is at rest, relative to you

$$M = \frac{M_0}{\sqrt{1 - \frac{v^2}{c^2}}}$$

And another result with mass is this: Mass may be converted to pure energy (such as light, X rays, gamma rays—no ashes or bits, just pure energy).

$$E = mc^2$$

where m is the vanished mass and E is the energy which appears.

All of these ideas and results have been confirmed by experiments.

The fast bodies that we use are tiny particles such as electrons and atomic nuclei, and their "flying" masses are easy to measure. In fact, the big cyclotrons which spin atomic particles to speeds nearly that of light are designed to take care of the fact that the masses of these flying particles do increase.

And you know that $E = mc^2$ comes true in A-bombs and H-bombs, where matter turns to pure energy; and $E = mc^2$ comes true also in nuclear reactors and atomic engines. The time effect has been confirmed in a number of ways. Here's one:

On earth, we can create certain particles called *mesons*. Some of them are radioactive, but die out very quickly. Now, the same particles also reach us from the sky, and they should have lost their radioactivity long ago, in space, before reaching us. But they arrive, emit their radiation, then die out. How come?

Time running slowly — sort of suspended animation

Clearly, because of their enormous speeds, their "time machine" is running very slowly.

2. *The General Theory of Relativity*. In this work, Einstein considered all sorts of motions, not just uniform motions in straight lines. He took into account gravitational effects, too.

One result is this: Gravitation is equivalent to acceleration, and vice versa. For example, if you are out in free space, very far away from any planets or stars, and if your spaceship is accelerated so that your velocity changes by thirty-two feet per second every second, then you might think that you are back on earth! This is so because you feel your normal earth weight. If you didn't know that the spaceship had been accelerated while you were sleeping, then, upon waking, you might step out onto "Earth!"

Einstein decided that gravitation is not really a force. He pointed out that we only feel it when we are prevented from executing free fall. Thus, when you stand on the floor, you feel gravity, or weight. But, if the floor should open up and you fall, you feel no gravity, no weight. In fact, you feel nothing until your journey suddenly ends.

Einstein thought of the earth or any other body as producing a certain condition in the space about it, invisible pathways for motion, or contours for flight. He called it a "curvature" of the space

A body will find its proper contour to follow, according to where it is released and with what speed. Thus

Such thoughts led Einstein to predict that light should find a contour, too, when it passes near a massive body. So he predicted that starlight, in passing near the sun, should be curved.

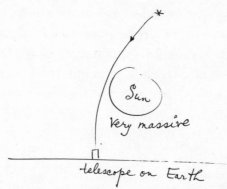

The sun *does* do this. It does curve the rays of light according to the amount that Einstein had calculated.

In his *General Theory* he also found an explanation for the amount of "rosetting" action that the Planet Mercury executes. Here's what I mean:

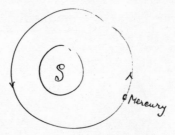

Mercury does not exactly retrace its orbit. The axis of its ellipse tilts, as the centuries pass.

Einstein explained the full effect mathematically.

3. *The Unified Field Theory.* Professor Einstein did not live long enough to find a mathematical connection among gravity, magnetism, and electricity—a kind of singleness, a unity. And this was to include large bodies and tiny atoms, as well. Gravity, magnetic effects, and electrical ones, each, in a sense, produce their own "curvatures" of space.

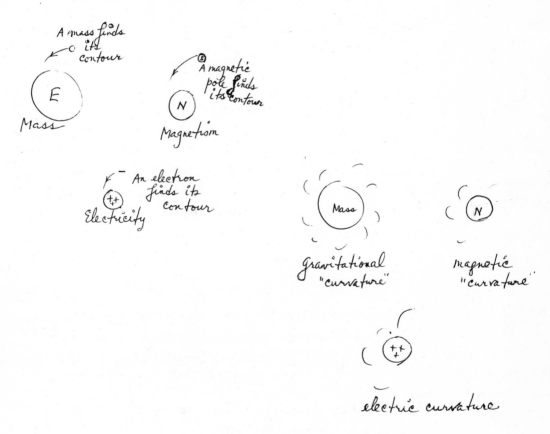

Are these curvatures interrelated? Are they really part of one grand curvature? Why don't magnetic or electric charges sense and respond to gravitational curvature?

As we said, Einstein did not finish the work of the *Unified Field Theory.* Maybe some young boy or girl now living will do this—will pick up where the grand old man left off.

He had had a hard time in his life because of the Jewish faith of his ancestry. It was not easy for him to get a higher education in Germany, and to find a professorship—except when he became famous. Even after his *Special Theory of Relativity* came out things were easier for him in Switzerland than in Germany. Marie Curie had to write a letter in his behalf, stating that any university which makes Einstein a part of its faculty will be fortunate—he has an unusual and original mind. . . .

Later in life Einstein wrote, "If my theory proves right, the Germans will say I am German, the French that I am Swiss . . . the British that I am European. . . .

"If it proves wrong, the Germans will say I am a Swiss Jew, the French that I am a German, and the British won't say anything."

Once, when Einstein was asked to write about his life, as a preface to a book relating to his scientific work, he said, "I am the type of man who deals with ideas, and the story of my life does not occupy my mind." He thereupon wrote a biographical sketch which was really a discussion of scientific concepts of interest to him.

So why don't we leave it at that, too—let his work speak for him. This is not to say that he wasn't interested in humanity. Nobody was interested more. Once, when I said to him that radiation might make tomatoes grow larger, Einstein replied, "That may be fine for tomatoes, but what if it happens to people—to their heads?"

He changed our universe—his work involves the atoms, and all space, too. Certainly, he had stood on the shoulders of giants before him.

Who will stand on his shoulders?